W9-ARO-669

Step-By-Step Repair Manual

It doesn't necessarily take a highly trained service technician to make most repairs on an appliance. This book shows you just how easy it can be to repair your own refrigerator. Whether you're an avid do-it-yourselfer or just a beginner, the step-by-step photo instructions and detailed explanations will help you perform the majority of refrigerator and freezer repairs you're likely to encounter.

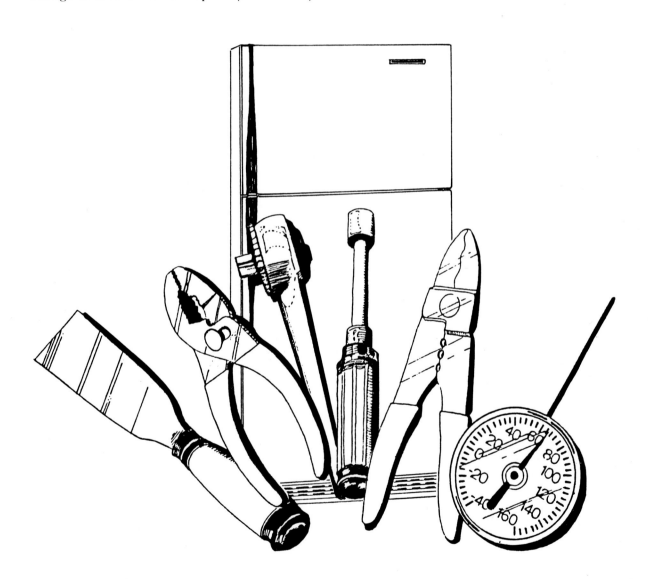

By learning to do as many of your own repairs as possible, you save time and money.

Safety Information: Refrigerators and freezers are complex electromechanical appliances. Any attempt to repair your refrigerator or freezer may, if improperly performed, result in personal injury and property damage. GE cannot be responsible for the interpretation of this manual, nor can it assume any liability in connection with its use. For more detailed safety information see page 2 of this manual.

If your appliance is still under warranty: Before you attempt any repairs, check to see if your appliance is covered under warranty. If you or any unauthorized service technician tries to repair an appliance under warranty, the warranty may be voided.

Step-by-Step Repair Manual for GE/Hotpoint
Refrigerators and freezers
General Electric Company

©1990 by General Electric Co.
    Appliance Park
    Louisville, KY 40225

Contents

Note: Pages 1 through 8 contain important information. Be sure to carefully read these pages before you begin any repair procedures.

How to use this manual

GE has recognized the growing need for the homeowner to perform as many of the service operations as possible around the house. Consequently, we have prepared this manual to provide the typical homeowner with the information necessary to perform the majority of refrigerator and freezer repairs. This manual is written in an easy to follow, step-by-step, photo guide format to instruct you how to do your own repairs.

Before you begin your repair

It is important that before you begin any repair or diagnosis on your appliance you take the time to read the general information on pages 2 through 8. By acquiring a basic understanding of refrigerator and freezer repair and important safety information, you'll be a step ahead on diagnosing and remedying the problem.

Problem Diagnostic Charts

When a problem does occur, refer to the Problem Diagnostic Chart section of the manual (pages 8-17). These charts will help you pinpoint your trouble by listing possible causes from the most likely to the least common cause. The charts will refer you to the repair procedures (pages 18-92) that use photography and illustrations to show you step-by-step how to remedy the problem. Be sure to read the entire repair procedure carefully before attempting any work.

Glossary of Terms

If you find a term you don't understand, you may find it listed in the Glossary of Terms listed at the end of this manual (pages 103-106). Also, don't forget to use the index as reference when searching for various information.

Read your *Use and Care Book*

After you have read the introductory sections in this manual, you may want to re-read the **Use and Care Book** that accompanies your appliance. The **Use and Care Book** can tell you how to remedy many problems that aren't due to equipment failures such as resetting the temperature control. It also contains information on maintenance and care and how to save energy. You may just discover that your refrigerator or freezer has useful features you may have forgotton.

Preventive Maintenance

When you have completed your repair, the Preventive Maintenance section (pages 94-95) can help you obtain the best results from your GE/Hotpoint refrigerator or freezer. Preventive maintenance is a vital key to long life for your appliance. The few minutes you invest in caring for your refrigerator or freezer properly can save you a great deal of time and trouble.

What repairs are covered?

Although GE has introduced hundreds of refrigerator and freezer models through the years , similarities in basic components allow this manual to cover most common repairs. Some procedures may not apply to your appliance; they may be applicable for only a particular model or brand (GE/Hotpoint). For example, your appliance may not have automatic defrost, but instead have a cycle-defrost operation that periodically will require manual defrosting of the freezer compartment. Both types of refrigerator models will be explained fully in this manual and major differences between models will be noted in the repair procedures.

Safety information

Refrigerators and freezers are complex electromechanical appliances. Any attempt to repair your appliance may, if improperly performed, result in personal injury and property damage. GE cannot be responsible for the interpretation of this manual, nor can it assume any liability in connection with its use.

> **Safety Precautions**
> To minimize the risk of personal injury or property damage it is important that the following safe service practices be observed:

1. **Be sure you are operating your refrigerator or freezer properly. Read carefully the *Use and Care Book* that comes with your appliance.**

2. **Know the location of your refrigerator or freezer's circuit breakers or fuses. Clearly mark all switches and fuses for quick reference. If you are unfamiliar with circuit breakers and fuses, please refer to Procedure #1: Inspecting Circuit Breakers and Fuses.**

3. **Before servicing your refrigerator or freezer, UNPLUG the power cord before performing any repairs or removing any access panel. Note: Except for Procedure #5: Temperature Testing, none of the repairs in this manual require voltage to be applied to the refrigerator or freezer during the repair procedure.**

4. **Be careful when handling refrigerator or freezer access panels, parts, or any components which may have sharp edges. Avoid placing your hand into any area of the appliance which you cannot first visually inspect for sharp edges.**

5. **Always use the correct tool for a job and be sure tools are in good condition. Worn, faulty, and misused tools can cause accidents.**

6. **Never interfere with or bypass the operation of any switch, component or feature of your refrigerator or freezer.**

7. **Use only replacement parts of the same size and capacity as the original part. If you have any questions, contact your authorized local appliance parts dealer.**

8. **When replacing any component, be sure any green ground wires are reconnected securely in their original positions to avoid danger of shock or short circuit.**

9. **Before reconnecting the power supply, make sure no uninsulated wires or terminals are touching the cabinet. Electrical wiring and all grounds must be correctly reconnected and secured away from sharp edges, components and moving parts. All panels and covers should be reinstalled before the refrigerator or freezer is plugged in.**

10. **The line cord must be plugged into a grounded, three prong receptacle. Never cut or remove the third (ground) prong from the power cord plug.**

11. **Do not substitute ordinary wire for any internal wiring of your refrigerator or freezer. The wire must carry heavy current and can be subjected to heat. It is especially important that all connections are tight and secure.**

12. **Carefully read through the entire repair procedure for a specific repair before attempting the job. If you don't fully understand the procedure or doubt your ability to complete it, call a qualified service technician.**

13. **Be sure all water connections for icemakers or dispensers are properly tightened on refrigerators with automatic icemakers or dispenser features.**

14. **When disposing of an old refrigerator or freezer, make sure the door or lid is removed to avoid the danger of a child being trapped inside.**

15. **Throughout this manual, additional safety precautions dealing with specific repair procedures will be presented. This information should be carefully read.**

Parts information

Obtaining replacement parts

If you're going to the time and trouble of repairing your appliance, it is important that you get the correct replacement part. First, be sure you have the complete model number for your appliance when ordering replacement parts. Even if you take in the original part, a salesperson may not be able to supply the correct replacement part without your complete model number. Second, to assure proper fit and performance, use Genuine GE Renewal Parts.

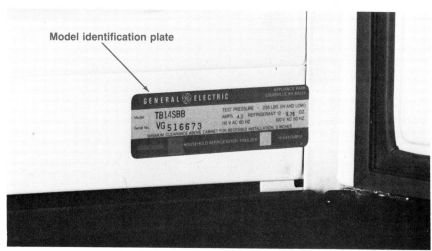

Model identification plate

The following photos show sample model identification plates. The model number represents coded manufacturing and engineering information that is important when ordering parts for your refrigerator or freezer.

GE identification plate

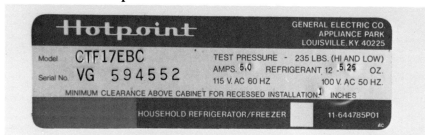

Hotpoint identification plate

Finding your model number

The model and serial numbers of your refrigerator or freezer are stamped on a metal model specification plate. On most refrigerators and upright freezers, you will find the model number inside the door at the lower right of the cabinet, just above the grille or cabinet base. On chest type freezers this identification plate can be located on the rear of the cabinet near the hinge. On some single door refrigerators, the identification plate will be found below the frozen food compartment at the left, just inside the appliance door.

The complete model number must be used when ordering exact replacement parts. Be sure to copy this number correctly and record it on page 93 of this manual for future reference.

Genuine GE Renewal Parts

All parts are not created equal when it comes to your GE or Hotpoint refrigerator or freezer. Some non-GE parts may require extra brackets and adaptors to make them fit. Others may not be designed for the exact electrical specifications of your appliance and, as a result, may cause substandard performance. With Genuine GE Renewal Parts you are assured a proper fit and performance match for the original part -- an assurance that's backed in writing with a one-year limited warranty.

For your convenience in obtaining parts, GE has company-owned parts stores and authorized parts dealers throughout the country. To find the outlet nearest you, look in the Yellow Pages under major headings, "Appliances-Household-Major" or "Refrigerators or Freezers," then subheads, "Service & Repair" or "Supplies & Parts." If you are unable to find where GE parts are sold in your area, call the GE Answer Center® consumer information service

Genuine GE Renewal Parts are backed by a one-year limited warranty to assure you proper fit and performance.

toll free, 800-626-2000 for assistance.

Some dealers feature the Quick Fix® system of GE common replacement parts and parts kits. Designed specifically for do-it-yourselfers, Quick Fix® parts come in clearly marked packages complete with hardware and step-by-step replacement instructions.

Whether it's the Quick Fix® system or the regular GE line of parts, you should insist on the performance and quality of Genuine GE Renewal Parts. After all, if you're investing time and money to care for your appliance, it's better to do it right the first time and not chance problems later from using an unsuitable part.

How your appliance operates

The purpose of this section is to give you some background on how a refrigerator or freezer operates. The more familiar you become with the operation of these appliances the easier it will become for you to understand the causes and solutions to a problem that might arise. For example, in order to chill foods you simply place them in the proper compartment, either the fresh food or freezer compartment. But, what causes the appliance to maintain the correct temperature and how does the cold air flow from the freezer compartment to the fresh food compartment? Answers to these questions could make it easier to repair your refrigerator or freezer, so let's take a closer look at exactly how they operate.

A refrigerator and freezer operate basically on the same principle. The temperature each maintains is the significant difference between these two appliances. The temperature differential is brought about by a partition in the refrigerator. Instead of one large frozen food compartment as in a freezer, a refrigerator is divided into compartments, fresh food and frozen food. The desired temperature is maintained in both compartments by the regulation of air flow from the freezer to the fresh food compartment through baffles and vents. In a home freezer, the temperatures are calibrated to maintain a near zero temperature.

It all starts at the power supply cord that connects your appliance to the wall receptacle. Inside the appliance cord there are three flexible wires. Two of these wires carry the electricity to a molded distribution plug. The third wire is the ground wire for safety purposes. The power is carried through an internal network of wiring and distributed to various parts of the refrigerator or freezer. The fundamental components of a refrigeration system are: the evaporator, condenser, compressor, and capillary tube. Every refrigeration system operates using some configuration of these basic parts.

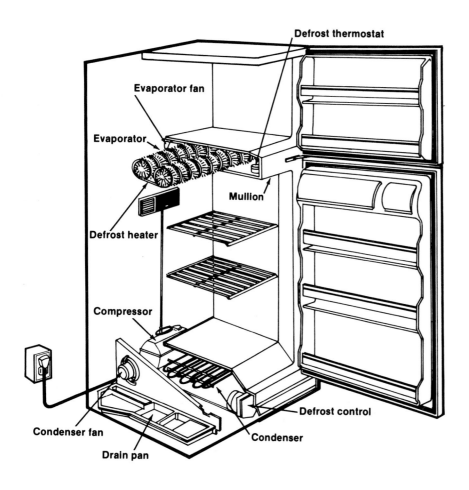

Defrost thermostat

Evaporator fan

Evaporator

Mullion

Defrost heater

Compressor

Defrost control

Condenser fan

Condenser

Drain pan

How your refrigerator or freezer cools

A refrigeration unit cools using the principle that liquid absorbs heat when it vaporizes. Your refrigerator or freezer contains a refrigerant chemical called R-12. This chemical has a boiling point of 22 degrees Fahrenheit. The chemical is colorless, odorless, and under normal conditions, non-toxic. These factors make it ideal for home refrigeration.

The refrigerant chemical is condensed into a liquid and then expanded into a gas. The compressor compresses the gas and pumps it into the condenser. The process of compressing heats the gas. The hot gas is above room temperature so the air flowing over the condenser coils cools the gas causing it to condense into a liquid. From the condenser, the liquid refrigerant passes through a small-diameter tube called a capillary tube. The capillary tube slowly meters the liquid refrigerant into the evaporator where it evaporates to produce the cooling effect. The refrigerant is then drawn out of the evaporator through a tube called the suction line by the compressor. The process repeats itself over and over again.

Defrost systems

In any refrigeration system there is frost. When warm, humid air entering your refrigerator is cooled, it collects in the form of frost. Frost freezes on the evaporator which is the coldest surface below the freezing point inside the

Refrigerating System

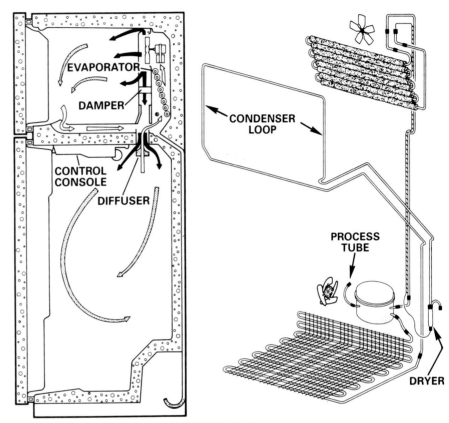

COLD AIR ■   MIXED AIR ▨   WARMER AIR ☐

refrigerator. Frost affects the operating efficiency of your appliance and must be removed. Frost is mainly caused by frequent opening and closing of the refrigerator door. There are three methods of removing frost from your refrigerator:

Manual Defrost: In this type of defrosting system you must set the temperature control to "defrost" or "off". You then wait until the refrigerator gets warm enough to melt the existing frost.

Cycle-Defrost: This is a combination of manual defrosting in the freezer and an automatic defrost in the fresh food compartment. The fresh food compartment never needs defrosting, but the frozen food compartment does. The cycle defrost system defrosts the fresh food compartment by not "cycling" on until the frost is gone.

No-Frost System: This type of refrigerator is automatically programmed to prevent the permanent formation of frost in both the freezer compartment and fresh food compartment. It is the most convenient system as no frost forms in either the refrigerator or the freezer compartment.

Models covered

Over the years, GE/Hotpoint has produced hundreds of various refrigerator and freezer models in several different configurations. Repairs on most models are similar, so most problems that may arise with your refrigerator or freezer are likely to be covered in this manual.

Exception: This manual does not cover repairs for electronic touch control mechanisms, but will apply for some standard component repairs on the "touch control and monitoring" refrigerators.

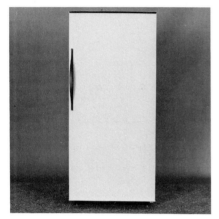

Single door conventional refrigerator has one outer door and a small inside door for the frozen food storage compartment, located above the main food compartment. Defrosting is manually initiated.

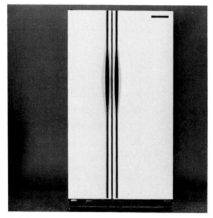

Side-by-side refrigerator/ freezer is the newest design in refrigerators. It offers extra large storage capacities in both the vertical freezer and the fresh food compartments.

Top mount cycle-defrost refrigerator/freezer, the most common refrigerator model, features a separate freezer compartment that must be manually defrosted. The fresh food compartment automatically defrosts each time the refrigerator cycles off.

Top mount automatic defrost refrigerator/freezer is a combination refrigerator/ freezer which is automatically programmed to prevent the permanent formation of frost in either the freezer compartment or fresh food compartment.

Upright freezer is designed for convenient frozen food storage in a limited space. Bookshelf storage doors as well as interior shelving keep frozen foods easily accessible and aid in visual inventory.

Chest freezer is the traditional freezer offering the largest capacity storage. Lift-out baskets in most models offer easy rotation of foods as well as convenient storage for items used often.

Problem diagnostic charts

How to use the problem diagnostic charts

The problem diagnostic charts help you with one of the most difficult tasks in do-it-yourself repairs...locating the possible causes and solutions to your problem. Before using the charts, make note of the problem you are experiencing with your refrigerator or freezer. Keen observation can often lead you to the area where the problem lies. Watch for anything that deviates from normal operation. Note everything that is or is not working. Once you have identified a problem, then you can begin to solve it by referring to the Problem Diagnostic Charts.

Each page of the Problem Diagnostic Charts has four columns of information: (1) **Problem**; (2) **Possible Cause**; (3) **Repair Procedure**; and (4) **Skill Level**. The first column, **Problem**, lists examples of problems you may encounter with your appliance. In the second column, there is a list of **Possible Causes** that may be the reason for the problem. The possible causes for each problem are listed in the order in which they might be expected to occur from the most likely to the least likely. A **Repair Procedure** for each possible cause is listed in column three. Repair procedure information refers you to a course of action to remedy the possible cause of your refrigerator or freezer problem.

The final column, **Skill Level**, indicates a skill level rating for each repair task. This rating will help you decide which repairs you feel confident of completing.

●	Easy	No previous experience needed
●●	Average	Requires removal of service panels. Mechanical ability is helpful.
●●●	Difficult	May require the use of an ohmmeter and/or splicing of electrical wires. Repair or replacement of component parts is more difficult.
●●●●	Very Difficult	May require the use of an ohmmeter and the ability to read a circuit diagram. Repair or replacement of component parts is complex.
●●●●●	Requires service technician	Requires special tools and skills

No matter what skill level assigned to a task, study the repair procedure and safety instructions carefully before proceeding.

NOTE: The problems listed below are numbered exactly as they appear in the PROBLEM column of the Problem Diagnostic Charts.

I. All refrigerator models
1. Refrigerator does not cool (compressor, lights do not operate)
2. Refrigerator does not cool (lights operate, compressor does not operate)
3. Refrigerator does not cool (lights and compressor operate)
4. Refrigerator not cool/cold enough (compressor, lights operate)
5. Refrigerator too cold
6. Refrigerator runs too much
7. Evaporator fails to defrost (automatic defrost models)
8. Interior light does not work
9. Water on floor
10. Ice in drain trough or water in liner bottom
11. Moisture on liner sides, shelves (sweating inside)
12. Moisture on cabinet or door exterior (sweating)
13. Frost builds up quickly on evaporator
14. Door out of alignment (not aligned with cabinet or other door)
15. Noisy operation
16. Odor in refrigerator
17. Breaker strips damaged
18. Shelves uneven or unsteady
19. Damaged trim
20. Damaged paint finish

II. Upright and chest freezers
21. Freezer not cold (compressor, lights do not operate)
22. Freezer does not cool (lights operate, compressor does not operate)
23. Freezer not cold (lights, compressor operate)
24. Freezer not cold enough
25. Freezer runs too much
26. Evaporator fails to defrost automatically (automatic defrost models)
27. Interior light does not work
28. Ice in liner bottom (automatic defrost model)
29. Frost builds up too quickly
30. Door out of alignment
31. Noisy operation
32. Damaged paint finish
33. Shelves uneven or unsteady
34. Breaker damaged by blow

III. Icemakers and dispensers
35. Intermittent or no icemaker operation
36. Ice cubes discolored or cloudy
37. Ice cubes too small
38. Poor ice rate (operation too slow)
39. Water on floor
40. Water or ice build up in freezer or bucket
41. Dispenser does not dispense water
42. Dispenser water unsatisfactory (water cloudy)

Problem diagnostic charts

I. ALL REFRIGERATOR MODELS

Problem	Possible Cause	Repair Procedure	Skill Level
1. Refrigerator does not cool (compressor, lights do not operate)	No power to refrigerator (open fuse or circuit breaker)	Check Power Supply (See p.19 & Procedure #1)	•
	Power cord defective (not plugged in, broken wire)	Check Power Cord (See p.21 & Procedure #2)	•••
	Open internal wiring (open wire or connector)	Check Wiring & Connections (See p.25 & Procedure #4)	•••
2. Refrigerator does not cool (lights operate, compressor does not operate)	Temperature control may be turned "OFF"	Check Temperature Control (See p.51 & Procedure #16)	•
	Temperature control defective	Check Temperature Control (See p.51 & Procedure #16)	••••
	Defrost control defective (stuck in defrost position)	Check Defrost Control (See p.61 & Procedure #19)	••••
	Relay defective (burned contacts or terminal)	Check Relay (See p.67 & Procedure #22)	••••
	Guardette® protector defective (open or broken wire)	Check Guardette® protector (See p.71 & Procedure #23)	••••
	Open internal wiring (open wire or connector)	Check Wiring & Connections (See p.25 & Procedure #4)	•••
	Compressor defective (windings burned out)	Check Compressor (See p.73 & Procedure #24)	••••
	Compressor defective	CALL SERVICE TECHNICIAN	•••••
3. Refrigerator does not cool (lights and compressor operate)	Refrigerant leak (loss of refrigerant)	CALL SERVICE TECHNICIAN	•••••
	Refrigeration system restricted (system contaminated)	CALL SERVICE TECHNICIAN	•••••
	Compressor defective (broken valve, internal leak)	CALL SERVICE TECHNICIAN	•••••
4. Refrigerator not cool/cold enough (compressor, lights operate)	Temperature control set too low	Check Temperature (See p.27 & Procedure #5)	•
	Dirty condenser (clogged with lint, dust)	Clean Condenser (See p.31 & Procedure #7)	•
	Condenser fan defective (no air flow over condenser)	Check Condenser Fan (See p.49 & Procedure #15)	•••
	Evaporator fan defective (no air flow over evaporator)	Check Evaporator Fan (See p.57 & Procedure #18)	••••

Skill Level Index: •Easy ••Average •••Difficult ••••Very Difficult •••••Requires service technician

9

Problem	Possible Cause	Repair Procedure	Skill Level
4. Refrigerator not cool/cold enough; compressor, lights operate (continued)	Defrost control defective (evaporator frost clogged)	Check Defrost Control (See p.61 & Procedure #19)	••••
	Defrost heater defective (evaporator frost clogged)	Check Defrost Heater (See p.65 & Procedure #21)	••••
	Defrost thermostat defective (evaporator frost-clogged)	Check Defrost Thermostat (See p.63 & Procedure #20)	••••
5. Refrigerator too cold	Temperature control set too high	Check Temperature (See p.27 & Procedure #5)	•
	Temperature control defective	Check Temperature Control (See p.51 & Procedure #16)	••••
6. Refrigerator runs too much	Temperature control set too high	Check Temperature (See p.27 & Procedure #5)	•
	Dirty condenser (clogged with lint, dust)	Clean Condenser (See p.31 & Procedure #7)	•
	Door gasket not sealing (gasket torn, not sealing)	Check Door Gasket (See p.41 & Procedure #12)	•••
	Door improperly adjusted (door not closing properly)	Check Door Alignment (See p.39 & Procedure #11)	••
	Condenser fan defective (no air flow over condenser)	Check Condenser Fan (See p.49 & Procedure #15)	•••
	Light switch defective (light stays on when door is closed)	Check Switch (See p.47 & Procedure #14)	•••
	Temperature control defective	Check Temperature Control (See p.51 & Procedure #16)	••••
7. Evaporator fails to defrost automatically (automatic defrost models)	Defrost control defective (won't advance, contacts burned)	Check Defrost Control (See p.61 & Procedure #19)	••••
	Defrost heater defective (open element)	Check Defrost Heater (See p.65 & Procedure #21)	••••
	Defrost thermostat defective (open contacts)	Check Defrost Thermostat (See p.63 & Procedure #20)	••••
	Open internal wiring (open wire or connector)	Check Wiring & Connections (See p.25 & Procedure #4)	•••

Skill Level Index: • Easy •• Average ••• Difficult •••• Very Difficult ••••• Requires service technician

Problem diagnostic charts (continued)

Problem	Possible Cause	Repair Procedure	Skill Level
8. Interior light does not work	Light bulb burned out	Check Light Bulb (See p.47 & Procedure #14)	•
	Light switch defective (open contacts)	Check Light Switch (See p.47 & Procedure #14)	•••
	Open internal wiring (open wire or connector)	Check Wiring & Connections (See p.25 & Procedure #4)	•••
9. Water on floor	Drain pan mispositioned	Check Drain Pan (See p.29 & Procedure #6)	•
	Drain pan defective (pan cracked, split, leaking)	Check Drain Pan (See p.29 & Procedure #6)	•
	Leaking water valve (fitting may be loose)	Check Water Valve (See p.75 & Procedure #25)	••••
10. Ice in drain trough or water in liner bottom	Drain tube stopped or clogged	Check and Clean Drain Tube (See p.29 & Procedure #6)	•
	Water leaking from icemaker	Check Icemaker Seal (See p.89 & Procedure #29)	••••
11. Moisture on liner sides, shelves (sweating inside)	Door gasket defective (gasket torn, not sealing)	Check Door Gasket (See p.41 & Procedure #12)	•••
	Door improperly adjusted (door not closing properly)	Check Door Alignment (See p.39 & Procedure #11)	••
	Liner heater defective	CALL SERVICE TECHNICIAN	•••••
12. Moisture on cabinet or door exterior (sweating)	Energy Saver switch improperly set	Check Switch Setting (See p.95 & Preventive Maintenance)	•
	Door gasket defective (gasket torn, not sealing)	Check Door Gasket (See p.41 & Procedure #12)	•••
	Cabinet heater defective	CALL SERVICE TECHNICIAN	•••••
	Insulation wet	Check Insulation--Remove Breaker Strips (See p.33 & Procedure #8)	•••
13. Frost builds up quickly on evaporator	Door gasket defective (gasket torn, not sealing)	Check Door Gasket (See p.41 & Procedure #12)	•••
	Door improperly adjusted (door not closing properly)	Check Door Alignment (See p.39 & Procedure #11)	••

Skill Level Index: •Easy ••Average •••Difficult ••••Very Difficult •••••Requires service technician

Problem	Possible Cause	Repair Procedure	Skill Level
14. Door out of alignment (not aligned with cabinet or other door)	Cabinet not level (unlevel, floor uneven)	Check Cabinet Level (See p.39 & Procedure #11)	•
	Door improperly adjusted (out of alignment)	Check Door Alignment (See p.39 & Procedure #11)	••
15. Noisy operation	Cabinet not level	Check Cabinet Level (See p.39 & Procedure #11)	•
	Drain pan rattling	Check Drain Pan (See p.29 & Procedure #6)	•
	Compressor loose in mounts (front or rear)	Check Compressor (See p.73 & Procedure #24)	•••
	Condenser fan motor defective	Check Condenser Fan (See p.49 & Procedure #15)	•••
	Evaporator fan motor defective	Check Evaporator Fan Motor (See p.57 & Procedure #18)	••••
16. Odor in refrigerator	Uncovered food	Store food properly (See p.94 & Preventive Maintenance)	•
	Accumulated spills or food particles	Clean refrigerator (See p.95 & Preventive Maintenance)	•
	Drain pan and drain tube need cleaning	Check Drain Pan (See p.29 & Procedure #6)	•
17. Breaker strips damaged	Breaker strip cracked	Remove and Replace Breakers (See p.33 & Procedure #8)	•••
18. Shelves uneven or unsteady	Shelf supports damaged or missing	Replace Shelf Supports (See p.35 & Procedure #9)	••
19. Damaged trim	Trim damaged or missing (handles damaged)	Replace Trim or Handles (See p.37 & Procedure #10)	••
20. Damaged paint finish	Finish discoloration	Clean and Polish (See p.45 & Procedure #13)	•
	Scratches and nicks	Retouch Affected Area (See p.45 & Procedure #13)	•
	Cabinet or door finish damaged or rusting (large area)	Respray Cabinet, Doors (See p.45 & Procedure #13)	••

Skill Level Index: • Easy •• Average ••• Difficult •••• Very Difficult ••••• Requires service technician

Problem diagnostic charts (continued)

II. UPRIGHT AND CHEST FREEZERS

Problem	Possible Cause	Repair Procedure	Skill Level
21. Freezer is not cold (compressor, lights do not operate)	No power to freezer (open fuse or circuit breaker)	Check Power Supply (See p.19 & Procedure #1)	•
	Power cord defective (not plugged in, broken wire)	Check Power Cord (See p.21 & Procedure #2)	•••
	Open internal wiring (open wire or connector)	Check Wiring & Connections (See p.25 & Procedure #4)	•••
22. Freezer does not cool (lights operate, compressor does not operate)	Temperature control turned to "OFF"	Check Temperature Control (See p.51 & Procedure #16)	•
	Temperature control defective	Check Temperature Control (See p.51 & Procedure #16)	••••
	Defrost control defective (stuck in defrost position)	Check Defrost Control (See p.61 & Procedure #19)	••••
	Relay defective (burned contacts or terminal)	Check Relay (See p.67 & Procedure #22)	••••
	Guardette® protector defective (broken wire or open)	Check Guardette® Protector (See p.71 & Procedure #23)	••••
	Open internal wiring (open wire or connector)	Check Wiring & Connections (See p.25 & Procedure #4)	•••
	Compressor inoperative	Check Compressor (See p.73 & Procedure #24)	••••
	Compressor defective	CALL SERVICE TECHNICIAN	•••••
23. Freezer is not cold (compressor, lights do not operate)	Refrigerant leak (loss of refrigerant)	CALL SERVICE TECHNICIAN	•••••
	Refrigeration system restricted (system contaminated)	CALL SERVICE TECHNICIAN	•••••
	Compressor defective (broken valve, internal leak)	CALL SERVICE TECHNICIAN	•••••

Skill Level Index: • **Easy** •• **Average** ••• **Difficult** •••• **Very Difficult** ••••• **Requires service technician**

Problem	Possible Cause	Repair Procedure	Skill Level
24. **Freezer not cold enough**	Temperature control set too low	Check Temperature (See p.27 & Procedure #5)	•
	Dirty condenser (some upright models)	Clean Condenser (See p.31 & Procedure #7)	•
	Condenser fan defective (some upright models)	Check Condenser Fan (See p.49 & Procedure #15)	•••
	Evaporator fan defective (automatic defrost models)	Check Evaporator Fan (See p.57 & Procedure #18)	••••
	Defrost control defective (evaporator frost-clogged)	Check Defrost Control (See p.61 & Procedure #19)	••••
	Defrost heater defective (evaporator frost-clogged)	Check Defrost Heater (See p.65 & Procedure #21)	••••
	Defrost thermostat defective (evaporator frost-clogged)	Check Defrost Thermostat (See p.63 & Procedure #20)	••••
25. **Freezer runs too much**	Temperature control set too high	Check Temperature (See p.27 & Procedure #5)	•
	Dirty condenser (some upright models)	Clean Condenser (See p.31 & Procedure #7)	•
	Door gasket defective (gasket torn, not sealing)	Check Door Gasket (See p.41 & Procedure #12)	•••
	Door improperly adjusted (door not closing properly)	Check Door Alignment (See p.39 & Procedure #11)	••
	Condenser fan defective (no air flow over condenser)	Check Condenser Fan (See p.49 & Procedure #15)	•••
	Light switch defective (light stays on when door is closed)	Check Light Switch (See p.47 & Procedure #14)	•••
	Temperature control defective	Check Temperature Control (See p.51 & Procedure #16)	••••

Skill Level Index: • **Easy** •• **Average** ••• **Difficult** •••• **Very Difficult** ••••• **Requires service technician**

Problem diagnostic charts (continued)

Problem	Possible Cause	Repair Procedure	Skill Level
26. Evaporator fails to defrost automatically (automatic defrost models)	Defrost control defective (won't advance, contacts burned)	Check Defrost Control (See p.61 & Procedure #19)	••••
	Defrost heater defective (open element)	Check Defrost Heater (See p.65 & Procedure #21)	••••
	Defrost thermostat defective (open contacts)	Check Defrost Thermostat (See p.63 & Procedure #20)	••••
	Open internal wiring (open wire or connector)	Check Wiring & Connections (See p.25 & Procedure #4)	•••
27. Interior light does not work	Light bulb burned out	Check Light Bulb (See p.47 & Procedure #14)	•
	Light switch defective (open contacts)	Check Light Switch (See p.47 & Procedure #14)	•••
	Open internal wiring (open wire or connector)	Check Wiring & Connections (See p.25 & Procedure #4)	•••
28. Ice in liner bottom (automatic defrost model)	Drain tube stopped or clogged	Check & Clean Drain Tube (See p.29 & Procedure #6)	•
29. Frost builds up quickly	Door gasket defective (gasket torn, not sealing)	Check Door Gasket (See p.41 & Procedure #12)	•••
	Door improperly adjusted (door not closing properly)	Check Door Alignment (See p.39 & Procedure #11)	••
30. Door out of alignment	Cabinet not level	Check Cabinet Level (See p.39 & Procedure #11)	•
	Door improperly adjusted (out of alignment)	Check Door Alignment (See p.39 & Procedure #11)	••

Skill Level Index: •Easy ••Average •••Difficult ••••Very Difficult •••••Requires service technician

Problem	Possible Cause	Repair Procedure	Skill Level
31. **Noisy operation**	Cabinet not level	Check Cabinet Level (See p.39 & Procedure #11)	•
	Drain pan rattling	Check Drain Pan (See p.29 & Procedure #6)	•
	Compressor loose in mounts (front or rear)	Check Compressor (See p.73 & Procedure #24)	• • •
	Condenser fan motor defective (some upright models)	Check Condenser Fan (See p.49 & Procedure #15)	• • •
	Evaporator fan motor defective (automatic defrost models)	Check Evaporator Fan (See p.57 & Procedure #18)	• • • •
32. **Damaged paint finish**	Finish discoloration	Clean and Polish (See p.45 & Procedure #13)	•
	Scratches and nicks	Retouch Affected Areas (See p.45 & Procedure #13)	•
	Cabinet or door finish damaged or rusting (large area)	Respray Cabinet, Doors (See p.45 & Procedure #13)	• •
33. **Shelves uneven or unsteady (not holding in place)**	Shelf supports damaged or missing	Replace Shelf Supports (See p.35 & Procedure #9)	• •
34. **Breaker strip cracked**	Breaker damaged by blow	Replace Breaker Strip (See p.33 & Procedure #8)	• • •

Skill Level Index: • Easy •• Average ••• Difficult •••• Very Difficult ••••• Requires service technician

Problem diagnostic charts (continued)

III. ICEMAKERS AND DISPENSERS

Problem	Possible Cause	Repair Procedure	Skill Level
35. Intermittent or no operation	Icemaker control turned to "OFF" position	Check Icemaker Control (See p.85 & Procedure #28)	•
	Icemaker power cord making poor connection	Check Icemaker Power Cord (See p.85 & Procedure #28)	•
	No water supply to icemaker	Check Water Supply (See p.75 & Procedure #25)	••••
	Icemaker motor defective	CALL SERVICE TECHNICIAN	•••••
36. Ice cubes discolored or cloudy	High mineral content in water	Check Water Supply, Add Filter (See p.77 & Procedure #26)	•••
37. Ice cubes too small	Inadequate water supply	Check Water Supply (See p.75 & Procedure #25)	••••
38. Poor ice rate (operation too slow)	Temperature in freezer too high (setting incorrect)	Check Temperature (See p.27 & Procedure #5)	•
39. Water on floor	Water line fittings loose	Check Valve Fittings (See p.75 & Procedure #25)	••
	Water valve leaking	Check Water Valve (See p.75 & Procedure #25)	••••
	Water dispenser reservoir or tubing leaking	Check Reservoir (See p.81 & Procedure #27)	••••
40. Water or ice build-up in freezer or bucket	Fill cup not sealed to mold	Check Fill Cup Seal (See p.89 & Procedure #29)	•••
	Mold seal leaking	Check Mold Seal (See p. 89 & Procedure #29)	••••
41. Dispenser does not dispense water properly	Inadequate water supply	Check Water Supply (See p.75 & Procedure #25)	••••
	Reservoir and/or tubing leaking or frozen	Check Reservoir & Tubing (See p.82 & Procedure #27)	••••
	Faulty water dispenser switch	Check Dispenser Switch (See p.82 & Procedure #27)	••••
	Leak in internal dispenser tubing	CALL SERVICE TECHNICIAN	•••••
42. Dispenser water unsatis-factory (water cloudy)	High mineral content in water	Check Water Supply, Add Filter (See p.77 & Procedure #26)	•••

Skill Level Index: • Easy •• Average ••• Difficult •••• Very Difficult ••••• Requires service technician

Repair procedures

How to use repair procedures

The following refrigerator and freezer repair procedures take you step-by-step through repairs for most of the problems you are likely to encounter with your appliance. The Problem Diagnostic Charts on pages 8-17 will help you to pinpoint the likely causes of your problem. Beginning with the most likely cause, you can then refer to the appropriate repair procedure section. The Repair Procedures are divided into two basic categories: repairs that apply to all model refrigerators and freezers, and repairs that relate to icemakers and water dispensers.

Each repair procedure is a complete inspection and repair process for a single component, containing the information you need to test a component that may be faulty and to replace it, if necessary. This format breaks down even some of the most complex repair problems into separate, easy-to-handle units. Following the instructions given, you can test each component separately, isolating the cause of the problem and replacing any faulty parts. If one procedure fails to locate the failed component, you simply refer back to the Problem Diagnostic Charts for the next most likely cause of the problem.

Featuring a close-up photograph of the component you will be testing, the repair procedure begins with a description of what the component does and how it works. In the case of a component which varies with different refrigerator or freezer models, you will be shown how to determine which type is found on your appliance.

Instructions showing how to test and replace the component begin with steps that must be followed to assure your safety. Other initial steps indicate the skills and equipment that will be needed for the task. If you are uncertain about a process that will be used, such as reading a circuit diagram, using an ohmmeter, or removing access panels, you are referred to the pages in this manual where that process is discussed in detail. No matter what your skill level, careful attention must be paid to these instructions and safety precautions before you begin any procedure.

Clear photographs of typical refrigerator or freezer models illustrate each step of every repair procedure, proceeding from visual inspection and testing to replacement of the component. Because of the diversity of refrigerator and freezer models available, your appliance may differ somewhat from the illustrated model. However, each procedure has been carefully designed to be representative of the entire GE/Hotpoint lines, and as much information as possible has been included to help you make repairs on most GE/Hotpoint refrigerators and freezers.

NOTE:
The repair procedures are listed below in the order in which they appear in this section. Refer to the Problem Diagnostic Charts on pages 8-17 for the procedure most likely to remedy your problem, then use this list to locate the desired procedure.

All refrigerator and freezer models
1. Circuit Breakers and Fuses
2. Power Connections
3. Access Panels
4. Wiring and Connectors
5. Temperature Testing
6. Drain Pan Cleaning
7. Condenser Cleaning
8. Breaker Strips
9. Shelf Supports
10. Door Handles and Hinges
11. Door Alignment
12. Door Gaskets
13. Cabinet Cosmetics
14. Light and Fan Switches
15. Condensor Fan
16. Temperature Control
17. Evaporator Cover Removal
18. Evaporator Fan
19. Defrost Control
20. Defrost Thermostat
21. Defrost Heaters
22. Relay
23. Guardette® Protector
24. Compression Motor

Icemakers and Dispensers
25. Water Valve
26. Water Filter
27. Dispenser Switch and Reservoir
28. Icemaker
29. Icemaker Cup and Mold Seal

Procedure 1
Inspecting circuit breakers and fuses

Electricity produced by the power company is delivered to your house through a series of connecting power lines. A power supply distribution panel is located at the point where the main line from the power company enters your home. One of two types of distribution panels services your household; either a circuit breaker panel or fuse panel. From the distribution panel the power line is divided into a number of smaller circuits which are distributed to various household appliances, receptacles, and lights. Each of these circuits is protected from becoming overloaded by either a circuit breaker or fuse.

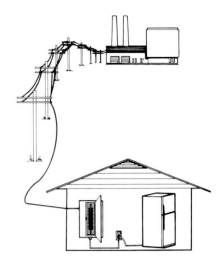

Circuit breaker type panel

Fuse type panel

It's important to know which breakers or fuses protect each circuit in your home. It is also wise to label them when everything is operating, so you'll know which breaker or fuse to look for in time of trouble.

The distribution panel is the first place to look when problems occur with your refrigerator or freezer. A tripped circuit breaker or blown fuse is a minor problem, but it can stop your refrigerator or freezer from working.

Note: If you are unable to identify the location of the circuit breakers or fuses that serve your refrigerator or freezer, contact a qualified electrician.

Step 1: UNPLUG refrigerator or freezer. Never touch any grounded objects such as water pipes when working around power supply. Stand on a dry insulated surface such as a dry board.

Step 2: This procedure requires the use of an ohmmeter. For instructions, please refer to Tools and Testing Equipment, page 98.

Step 3: Other than opening the door to the distribution panel, never remove any cover or expose any electrical terminals.

Step 4: <u>Circuit breakers:</u> Circuit breaker distribution panels contain rows of switches. When a breaker "trips", power is shut off and the breaker switch moves to an intermediate position between the "ON" and "OFF" points.

Step 5: To restore power, turn the breaker switch to the "OFF" position, then back to "ON". If the breaker trips again, the circuit is still overloaded. Further exploration of the problem is necessary before power can be restored.

Step 6: <u>Fuses:</u> A second type of distribution panel is protected by fuses. The large fuses are for appliances that require 220 volt, heavy current wiring. The smaller glassfront fuses are for 110 volt circuits and will be used for refrigerators and freezers.

Step 7: A separate branch circuit should be used for a refrigerator or freezer. This is recommended for best performance and to prevent overloading of wiring circuitry.

Step 8: Fuses for your refrigerator or freezer can simply be screwed in or out by hand. Be sure the fuse is screwed in tightly when checking or changing the fuse.

Step 9: Faulty or blown fuses cannot always be discovered simply by looking. Some will be obviously blown while others will have subtle changes within that can interrupt the flow of current.

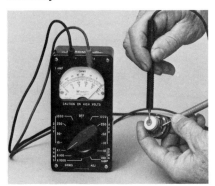

Step 10: Fuses can be checked with ohmmeter. With fuse removed set the meter to the lowest resistance scale then touch probes to brass tip and shell at the base of the fuse. If there is no continuity, replace.

Step 11: Screw in new fuse being certain not to use a fuse any larger than specified by the manufacturer. Replacing a fuse with a larger size can be dangerous.

Procedure 2
Inspecting and replacing power cord

Skill Level Rating: | Easy | Average | **Difficult** | Very Difficult |

Most electrical appliances in your home have a power cord and plug to carry current from the wall receptacle to your appliance. The power cord on a refrigerator or freezer is a three-wire grounding type cord. It is polarized to coincide with a properly polarized and grounded wall receptacle. The round pin terminal of the plug mates with the earth ground supplied to the wall receptacle. The round pin terminal is connected to the green center conductor of the power cord, which is attached to the product forming a chassis ground. The two flat blade terminals of the power cord mate with the hot and neutral line terminals of the wall receptacle to provide a voltage source circuit for the appliance. The neutral conductor of the power cord is identified by either molded ribs or dashed lines on the insulation covering the conductor.

If your refrigerator or freezer fails to operate properly, one of the first areas to examine is the power cord. Most problems of the power cord are caused by damage and loose connections and will likely be visible.

Power cord

21

Power cord (continued)

Step 1: Always exercise safe work habits when repairing or testing any electrical appliance. All access covers, ducts, grilles should be in place while refrigerator or freezer is operating.

Step 2: Care should be taken in moving your appliance away from the wall. Protect your floor covering from damage. On models with rollers, be sure to pull the appliance straight out.

Step 3: Pull plug from receptacle with firm, quick tug. Always grasp by plug and never by cord to prevent cord damage. Be careful not to contact blades of plugs with fingers.

Step 4: Inspect plug carefully for burns, corrosion or visible breaks. Look carefully around molded portion for signs of overheating. If plug is damaged, replace cord.

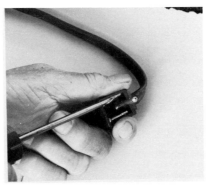

Step 5: If plug feels warm or feels loose in wall receptacle, there is a poor connection. Open up blades of plug by inserting a thin blade screwdriver in plug terminal. This will make a better contact.

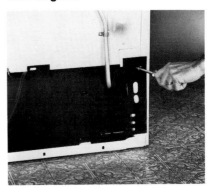

Step 6: Remove rear access panel and strain relief clamp. If you are unfamiliar with this process, please refer to Procedure #3: Removing Access Panels.

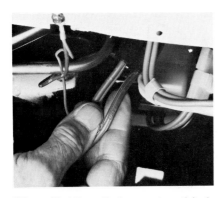

Step 7: Visually inspect molded power cord connection to wiring harness. If it shows any sign of breakage, burns, or other damage, replace power cord. To replace power cord, cut old cord inside appliance. Strip wire using directions from Procedure #4.

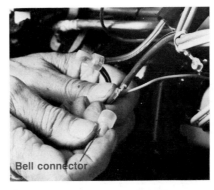

Bell connector

Step 8: Attach neutral wire on new power cord to orange harness wire. Neutral side is identified by molded ribs or dashed lines on insulation. Hot wire attaches to brown harness wires. Splice wires with bell connectors and crimp on tightly with crimping tool.

Ground wire

Step 9: Attach green ground wire to original location using original screw. CAUTION: Failure to connect power cord leads and ground wire as described could create a shock hazard. Reassemble refrigerator or freezer and reconnect power supply.

Procedure 3
Removing access panels

Skill Level Rating: | Easy | **Average** | Difficult | Very Difficult

For reasons of safety and appearance, all electrical and mechanical components of a refrigerator or freezer are covered by access panels. These panels are usually attached with hex head screws. This section will familiarize you with the location of different panels and their removal.

Access panels

Step 1: UNPLUG the refrigerator or freezer from the wall receptacle. Watch for sharp edges inside machine compartment.

Step 2: Care should be taken in moving your appliance away from the wall. Protect your floor covering from damage. On models with rollers, be sure to pull the appliance straight out.

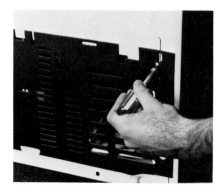

Step 3: Using a nutdriver, remove all hex head screws from fiber board panel at the bottom of the appliance. Remove panel taking care not to damage it.

Access panels (continued)

Step 4: Removing the lower access panel exposes wiring, power cord connection, compressor, and on some models the condenser fan.

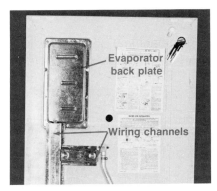

Step 5: Some models have metal channels that cover wiring and/or tubing. These are attached with hex head screws. Remove with a nut driver.

Step 6: The removal of these metal covers will give access to some external wiring and the rear of the evaporator. Some models have different cover configurations, but removal is basically the same.

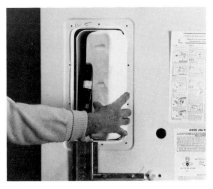

Step 7: On models with evaporator back plate, remove screws. Carefully pry back plate from outer case back. Avoid damaging back plate gasket. Grasp right side of foam block and rotate out of opening. Do not pry foam.

Step 8: When replacing back plate, check condition of gasket. Tighten screws in rotation sequence until the screws are hand tight. Cover must be sealed to back of refrigerator.

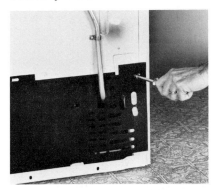

Step 9: When replacing fiber board panel, re-attach the power cord strain relief. Make sure all ground wires are reconnected.

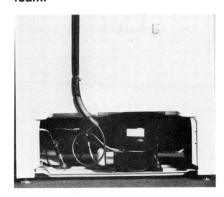

Step 10: Some upright freezers have open machine compartments. Others have access panels similar to refrigerators. Follow instructions for refrigerator access panel removal for these.

Step 11: Most chest freezers have open access panels at the rear. Some models have a metal side access cover held in place by screws.

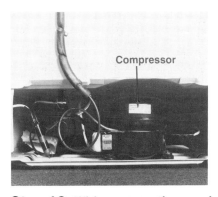

Step 12: Wiring connections and the compressor are located in the machine compartment. Basic components that may require servicing are usually located within this compartment.

Procedure 4
Repairing wiring and connections

Skill Level Rating: | Easy | Average | **Difficult** | Very Difficult |

Electrical current is carried to the switches, controls, and other components of your refrigerator or freezer by a network of color coded wires. Wiring connections to the components in a refrigerator or freezer are usually male and female push-on terminals. Any splicing of the wires is protected with a molded rubber covering or with connectors.

It is important that the wiring in your appliance is free from damage. A damaged wire, in addition to being a safety hazard, can cause a component to receive insufficient voltage for its proper operation. Any cut that reduces the diameter of the wire reduces the amount of current it will carry. This could affect the entire appliance by causing stress on other components. The damaged wire might also overheat and fail at the damaged point.

Note: If replacement wire is required, be sure to use only appliance wire having the same temperature and gauge rating as the wire you are replacing. Lengths of color coded wire are available from your authorized local appliance parts dealer.

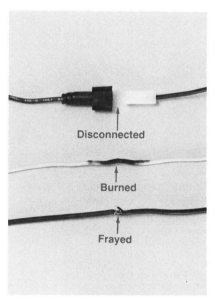

Damaged wires

Step 1: UNPLUG the refrigerator or freezer from the wall receptacle. Watch for sharp edges.

Step 2: This procedure requires the use of an ohmmeter. For instructions, please refer to Tools and Testing Equipment, page 98.

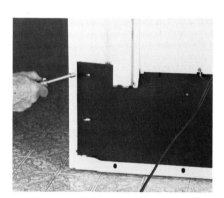

Step 3: This procedure requires the removal of access panels or breaker strips from your appliance. If you are unfamiliar with this process, please refer to Procedure #3: Removing Access Panels and/or Procedure #8: Removing Breaker Strips.

25

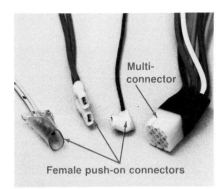

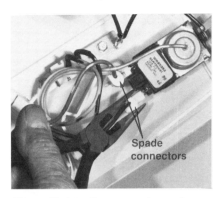

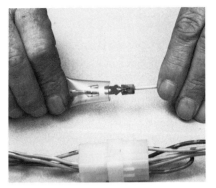

Step 4: Push-on spade connectors are typical of those used in refrigerator and freezer applications.

Step 5: To disconnect spade connectors, hold insulated cap firmly and pull off as you would disconnect a plug from a wall receptacle. Needle nose pliers can also be used. Take care not to damage wires or terminals.

Step 6: When reconnecting push-on terminals make sure you have a snug fit for a good connection. Take extra care to mate terminals in insulated cap connectors.

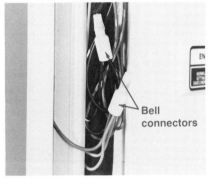

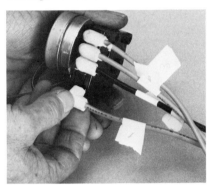

Step 7: Many models have wires spliced together with bell connectors. Frequently, these splices are located behind the breakers at the side of the fresh food compartment.

Step 8: When removing push-on connectors from terminals, label wires with tape or make a sketch of connections to assure proper installation when reassembling appliance.

Step 9: To test wire for continuity from connection point to connection point, refer to circuit diagram to isolate wire in question. Set ohmmeter to R x 1. Place probes at each end of wire to be tested. Needle should sweep upscale to zero.

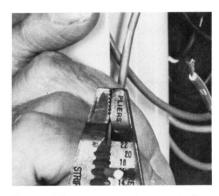

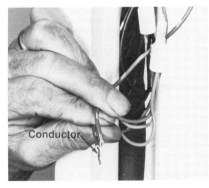

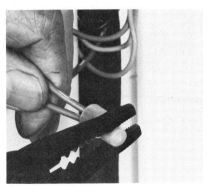

Step 10: To strip wire, use wire strippers. When stripping the insulation, be careful not to cut wire. Remove only enough insulation to make the splice. Usually 5/8″ is sufficient.

Step 11: The bare wire exposed is the conductor and should be bright and shiny for a good connection. Twist the two strands together with fingers.

Step 12: Place bell connector over twisted conductors and crimp tightly with crimping tool. Be sure skirt of connector fully covers all bare wire.

Procedure 5
Temperature testing

Skill Level Rating: | **Easy** | Average | Difficult | Very Difficult |

There are several basic jobs we ask our refrigerator or freezer to do. It must keep food cold enough to prevent spoilage, produce ice cubes, and hold certain foods in a frozen state.

Your refrigerator and freezer have essentially the same components and both operate on the same principle. Each, however, is designed to maintain certain temperatures for either the storage or freezing of food.

If you suspect your appliance has a cooling problem, it is important to take accurate temperature readings. Temperature readings can vary for several reasons. Take into consideration the time of day you are making your temperature test. Is it a busy part of the day when the refrigerator or freezer doors have been opened frequently? What is the ambient (room) temperature? Is the day extremely humid or warm? When you compare your readings with the ideal temperature range, all of these factors must be considered.

Note: Specific temperature data may be found in the technical service information pasted on the back of the refrigerator or freezer or inserted into an envelope behind the grille on some models. Remember when making temperature comparisons with this information, these are temperature tests made under ideal laboratory conditions with no door openings. Your readings may vary from this information.

Freezer compartment 0-8° Fahrenheit

Fresh food compartment 34-40° Fahrenheit

Temperature readings should be made in both compartments.

Step 1: Always exercise safe work habits when repairing or testing any electrical appliance. All access covers, ducts, grilles should be in place while refrigerator or freezer is operating.

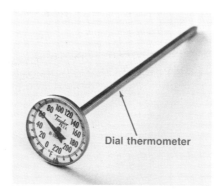

Dial thermometer

Step 2: A dial type refrigeration thermometer can be used to make this test. To check accuracy, immerse the probe in an ice bath, adjust dial to 32 degrees.

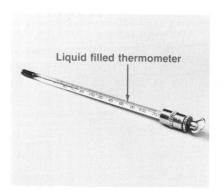

Liquid filled thermometer

Step 3: A liquid filled standard refrigeration type thermometer can also be used. Reading can be slightly more difficult to see with this type of thermometer, but it is less costly.

Temperature testing (continued)

Step 4: Temperature measurements should never be made in the air. Placing your thermometer on the shelf will not give you a proper indication. Temperatures fluctuate each time door is opened or during cycles.

Step 5: To test temperature in fresh food compartment, rinse off probe. Place probe in a liquid filled food container. This container must be in refrigerator 24 hours prior to testing. Read thermometer after 3 minutes.

Step 6: The ideal temperature reading in the fresh food compartment should be between 34 and 40 degrees Fahrenheit. These readings may vary, depending upon the time of day. Morning temperatures will usually be lower than those in the afternoon.

Step 7: Freezer temperature is best measured in ice cream that has been in the freezer for at least 24 hours prior to test. Insert probe, wait 2 minutes, remove and reinsert in different part of ice cream. Read after 3 minutes.

Step 8: If ice cream is unavailable, place thermometer between two frozen food packages. Close freezer door. Wait 4 minutes before taking reading.

Step 9: The ideal temperature for freezer compartment should be between 0 and 8 degrees Fahrenheit. On single door models, temperatures may be as high as 18 degrees Fahrenheit.

Step 10: Perform temperature testing on home freezers as on the freezer compartment of refrigerators. The ideal temperature range for a freezer is between 0 and 4 degrees Fahrenheit.

Procedure 6
Drain tube and drain pan cleaning

Skill Level Rating:

Easy	Average	Difficult	Very Difficult

Years ago in the era of the ice box, the ice man delivered great blocks of ice to his customers. These blocks of ice were placed in wooden ice boxes to keep food cold. As the ice in the ice box melted, the drain pan had to be emptied frequently. Today, because the drain pan does not have to be emptied frequently, we often forget to clean it periodically.

Water leaking on the floor under the refrigerator can be caused by a mispositioned or cracked drain pan. The drain tube can also overflow or ice over if it is blocked. Make a habit of cleaning the drain tube and drain pan on your appliance periodically.

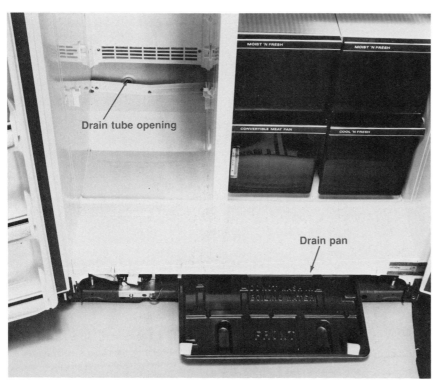

Drain tube and drain pan

Step 1: UNPLUG the refrigerator or freezer from the wall receptacle. Watch for sharp edges.

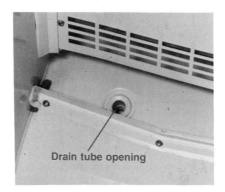

Step 2: The drain tube opening on many refrigerators is located at the bottom of the cabinet. Remove food and pans to expose the drain opening.

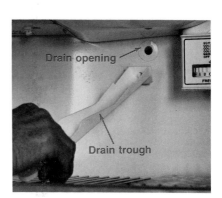

Step 3: On other models, drain tube is not readily visible. To expose tube, remove screw on drain trough. Pull through forward to disengage from drain tube opening at the rear of the liner.

Drain tube and pan (continued)

Step 4: The drain pan on most refrigerator models is concealed behind the grille. Remove grille to access. If you are unfamiliar with this process, refer to Procedure #7: Condenser Cleaning

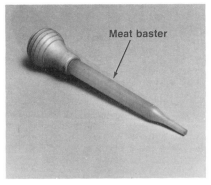

Meat baster

Step 5: Drain tube overflow or drain tube icing is usually due to bacteria growth or foreign particles inside the tube. To correct this condition, a meat baster with a slender tip and rubber bulb is used.

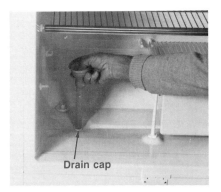

Drain cap

Step 6: Remove drain cap if necessary. Use the meat baster to force hot tap water (not boiling) through the drain tube to dislodge any obstruction in the tube. Then, clean the drain pan to remove residue.

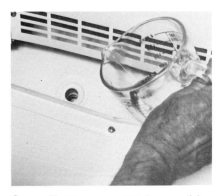

Step 7: To prevent this condition from recurring, pour a solution of baking soda (one teaspoon) and two cups hot (not boiling) water into the drain opening once or twice a year.

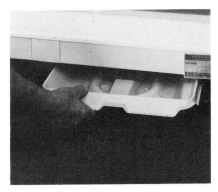

Step 8: Most drain pans can be removed by sliding pan toward you. Visually inspect pan for cracks or breaks. If pan is cracked or leaking from visible defect, replace pan.

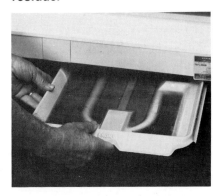

Step 9: To clean drain pan, remove any standing water inside pan. Wash pan with solution of one tablespoon baking soda to one quart warm water. Do not use boiling water or wash drain pan in dishwasher.

Step 10: Dry and replace drain pan. Reposition pan so it rests solidly on provided supports to prevent overflowing and pan rattle.

Step 11: Some drain pans are non-removable and are located at the rear of refrigerator. Move refrigerator out from wall to access. Do not remove this pan, but clean in place at least once a year.

Step 12: To clean non-removable drain pan, use a clean cloth or sponge dampened in a solution of one tablespoon baking soda and one quart warm water. Do not use abrasive cleaning powders or bleach.

Procedure 7
Condenser cleaning

Skill Level Rating:

Easy	Average	Difficult	Very Difficult

The condenser is one of the most important components in your refrigerator or freezer. It performs a vital service by condensing refrigerant vapors back to liquid form so the refrigerant can be reused in the cooling process. As these vapors are condensed, heat is discharged into the room.

The condenser is mounted either on the back of your appliance or is concealed behind the grille at the bottom of the cabinet. In some freezer models, it is built into the cabinet and is not visible. Though it is part of the sealed system and repairs to it require a service technician, cleaning the condenser using a long handled brush and vacuum cleaner can keep your refrigerator or freezer operating at peak efficiency. In time, household lint and dust can collect on the condenser. This will impede air flow and in turn decrease the efficiency of the appliance.

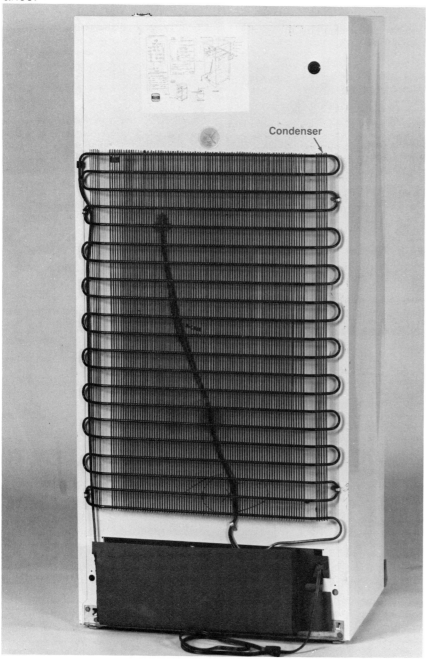
Condenser

Condenser mounted on rear of refrigerator

31

Condenser cleaning (continued)

Step 1: UNPLUG the refrigerator or freezer from the wall receptacle. Watch for sharp edges.

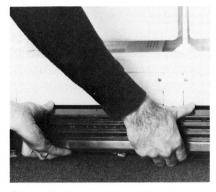

Step 2: To remove grille, grasp at bottom and pull up and out. To replace, set tabs on hooks at both ends and push top toward refrigerator until grille snaps in place. On some models you must push in on bottom.

Step 3: Some newer models have grilles that are attached with push-on sockets. These pull straight off or push on to replace. Look at your grille and make note of method of attachment for reinstallation.

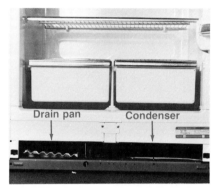

Step 4: The condenser coils and drain pan are concealed behind grille. Now is a good time to clean drain pan also. If you are unfamiliar with this process, refer to Procedure #6: Drain Tube and Pan Cleaning.

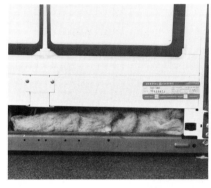

Step 5: Condenser coils should be kept free of dust and dirt for peak efficiency. Clean coils at least once a year, more often if you have long haired pets or area is particularly dusty.

Step 6: The condensor coils can be easily cleaned using a long handled brush as shown and your vacuum cleaner with a crevice attachment.

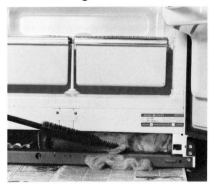

Step 7: Rake accessible dust outward using brush or vacuum tool. For thorough cleaning, you may remove rear access panel and clean from rear of refrigerator. See Procedure #3: Removing Access Covers.

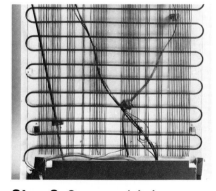

Step 8: Some models have condenser coils on back of appliance. Though not as prone to collect dust as models with coils on bottom, these models should be checked periodically for dust or obstructions.

Step 9: Some freezers have condenser coils mounted in same locations as refrigerators. Most, however, are located inside cabinet and do not require cleaning. Check model underneath and at back to be sure.

Procedure 8
Breaker strips

Skill Level Rating:

Easy	Average	**Difficult**	Very Difficult

Refrigerator and upright freezer cabinets consist primarily of the outer case, inner liner, and insulation. The outer case is painted steel. The liner in most models is steel, finished with porcelain or special paints. Some refrigerators use a separate liner for each compartment, but most models use a single liner with a dividing partition between the freezer and fresh food compartments.

Refrigerators and freezers with metal liners use breaker strips and/or breaker frames to prevent direct heat transfer from the outer case to the liner.

Breaker strips are made of various types of plastic and differ in size and shape according to the cabinet. Removal, however, is basically the same.

Note: Use extreme care when removing breaker strips to prevent breakage of strips. Removal of side-by-side breaker strips may cause damage to heaters. If you doubt your ability to perform this procedure, call a qualified service technician.

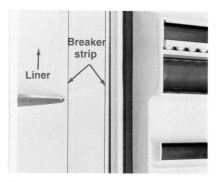

Breaker strips

Step 1: UNPLUG the refrigerator or freezer from the wall receptacle. Watch for sharp edges on clips and liner.

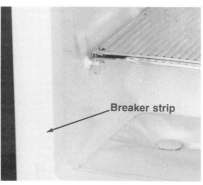

Step 2: Breaker strip mounting can differ on some models. Before attempting removal, make a careful visual examination.

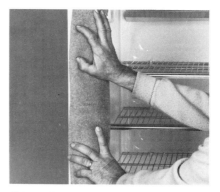

Step 3: Breaker strips are brittle when they are cold. To prevent breakage, bathe breaker strip with a hot bath towel to soften plastic before removing.

Step 4: Use a putty knife with masking tape wrapped around blade to prevent cabinet and breakers from being scratched or damaged.

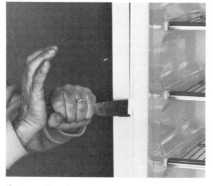

Step 5: Start with side breaker strip. A ridge along the breaker strip facilitates removal. Position putty knife against ridge. Bump handle of putty knife gently with heel of hand to disengage breaker from cabinet.

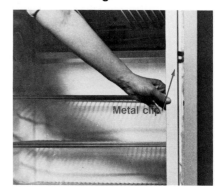

Step 6: As the front of breaker becomes disengaged, breaker can be pulled free from liner. Metal clips are sometimes used to hold breaker strips in place.

Breaker strips (continued)

Step 7: Remove any push-on leads attached to light switch located in some breakers. If you are unfamiliar with this process, please refer to Procedure #14: Light and Fan Switches.

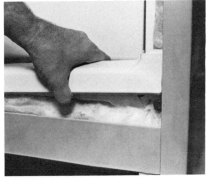

Step 8: To remove bottom breaker, start at one corner and disengage breaker strip in same manner as side breakers. As bottom breaker becomes disengaged, pull free from liner.

Step 9: To remove top breaker strip, grasp one end of breaker and pull out and down. Breaker will disengage from case flange and liner edge.

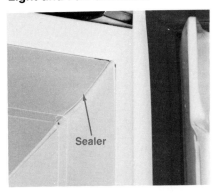

Step 10: Side-by-side. Some side-by-side models have sealer at the mitered corners. To remove breakers, cut through sealer carefully with sharp, thin knife.

Step 11: After sealer is cut, start at side breaker about 4″ from top. Gently pry the breaker strip down the entire length to disengage it from cabinet. After breaker is loose, pull from liner.

Step 12: Top mount refrigerator/freezer. Some models have a three-sided freezer breaker frame. To remove, first disengage sides with hands. Then grasp both sides and push in until top disengages from case flange.

Step 13: Chest freezer. To remove breaker strips, remove corner trim if separate from strip. Insert putty knife blade to release strip from edge of liner. Pull strip from case flange. Removal of lock catch may be necessary when removing front strip.

Step 14: To reinstall breakers, make sure insulation is in place. Start with bottom breaker. Position strip over edge of liner and in channel at front. Push until breaker is firmly in place.

Step 15: Next, replace side breakers fitting carefully at corners at bottom breaker to create a water-resistant joint. Complete with top breaker, bumping all breakers in place with heel of hand, if necessary.

Procedure 9
Replacing shelf supports

Skill Level Rating: | Easy | **Average** | Difficult | Very Difficult |

Wire shelves are used in most refrigerators and freezers. More deluxe refrigerators use glass shelves in the fresh food compartment. Plastic shelves are sometimes used, especially as covers for vegetable pans.

Various methods are used to support the shelves within the inner liner. Most commonly, peg or hook type supports, fastened into the liner near each corner of the shelf, secure the shelf in a fixed position. Cantilever type shelves are supported by perforated channels called "ladders", located at the rear of the liner.

Refrigerator shelf assembly

Step 1: UNPLUG the refrigerator or freezer from the wall receptacle. Watch for sharp edges.

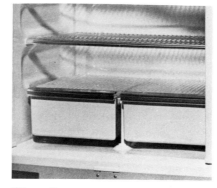

Step 2: Make a careful visual inspection of the shelf support system in your appliance before rearranging shelves or replacing supports.

Step 3: Because of the different types of support used, examine support before attempting to remove it, so as to prevent damaging appliance liner.

Shelf supports *(continued)*

Step 4: Cantilever type shelves are supported by perforated channels called "ladders" located at rear of liner. Hooks on shelves that engage the "ladders" permit simple rearranging of shelves.

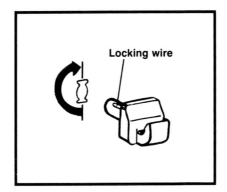

Step 5: The most commonly used support secures the shelf in a fixed position and is fastened into the liner near each corner of the shelf. These supports are held in place by a locking wire that engages the liner.

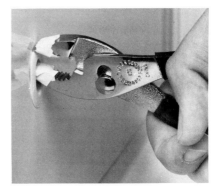

Step 6: To remove locking wire supports, turn clockwise to free wire clip from slot and pull out. Wrap plier jaws with tape to protect support. Install new support by inserting in slot upside down and turning clockwise 180° to secure.

Step 7: Some supports lift up and off of dovetail shaped base. The base is not removable on models that have a plastic liner. On models that have a metal liner, the base is removed as in Step 6.

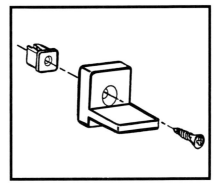

Step 8: Other models have supports secured by a screw passing through the support and into a grommet in the liner.

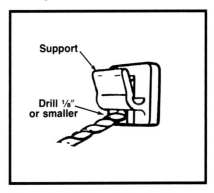

Step 9: Side-by-side shelf supports hook into a liner opening and lock into place with a tab on bottom of support. Carefully drill through base of support with 1/8" drill to cut through locking tab.

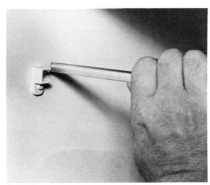

Step 10: Pan covers and drawers are often supported with channeled rails. Covers have dovetail design at rear which fits over rail allowing front to drop in place and conceal rail. Drawers slide on channels molded into plastic covers.

Step 11: Shelf supports in freezer compartment are much like those in fresh food compartment. The most commonly used supports feature locking wire clips. Turn clockwise while pulling out, taking care not to damage liner.

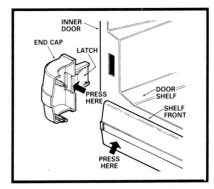

Step 12: Remove door shelf rails by first releasing end cap. Press latch and pull end cap out of slot. Release shelf from end cap by pressing firmly near the center of front while pulling from end cap pins. To reinstall rail, position over pins and press. Reinstall end cap into slot and press firmly until latch locks.

Procedure 10
Removing door handles and hinges

Skill Level Rating: | Easy | **Average** | Difficult | Very Difficult |

Removing or replacing door handles and hinges is not a difficult task. Most newer models have handles that can be removed from the door without removing the inner door panel. Handles with a magnetic latch require removal of the inner door panel to access mounting screws. Make an inspection of your model to determine the type of handles and method of mounting.

Hinges are usually secured to the cabinet with hex head screws that are readily visible. Some models have a cap over the top hinge that is held in place by a Phillips screw. The hinge cap may cover wiring that enters the door through a hollow hinge pin.

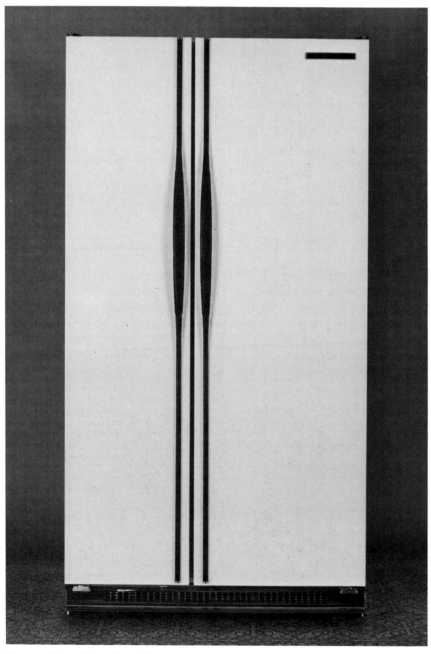

Decorative door handles

Door handles and hinges (continued)

Step 1: UNPLUG the refrigerator or freezer from the wall receptacle.

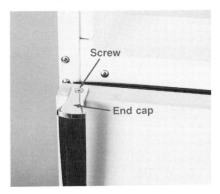

Step 2: Some door handles have removable end caps. Remove screw in larger end cap and lift end cap off. Remove screws securing handle to door.

Step 3: Push small end cap away from handle to expose screw. Remove screw to remove handle. Handle can then be replaced.

Step 4: To replace handle, align handle with screw holes. Insert screws and tighten. Replace end caps and end cap screws.

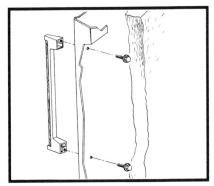

Step 5: Door handles on models with magnetic catch assemblies are secured from inside door. To remove this type handle, remove inner door panel. If you are unfamiliar with this process, please refer to Procedure #11: Door Alignment.

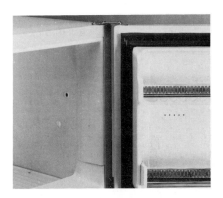

Step 6: Before removing door make a visual inspection of hinges. Top door must be removed before lower door. Remove top hinge screws. Lift door up to disengage from center hinge. Repeat process on bottom door.

Step 7: To replace door, position door on hinge pin. **Note:** Make sure nylon washers are used on hinge pins under door, and shims are between hinge and cabinet. After door is hung it must be realigned. Please refer to Procedure #11: Door Alignment.

Step 8: CAUTION: Chest freezer hinges are mounted under spring pressure. Hold hinge while removing screws. Gradually release pressure when screws are removed. Extreme care should be taken when removing hinges on chest freezers.

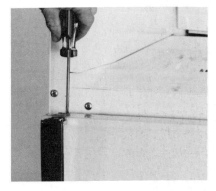

Step 9: Reassemble refrigerator or freezer and reconnect power supply.

Procedure 11
Door alignment

Refrigerator and upright freezer doors consist primarily of an outer door panel, inner door panel, insulation, and a gasket. The inner door panel is held to the outer door panel with screws located under the gasket flange. Metal retainer strips, when used, hold the door gasket and add stiffness to the edges of the inner door panel. Most models use fiberglass for door insulation. Some models, however, use poured foam insulation.

Diagonal cross braces are used in some upright freezers to add rigidity to the door. The braces are hooked into the upper corners of the outer door panel with adjustment screws located on the bottom edge of the outer door panel.

Note: The lid on most chest freezers is not rigid, which allows for self-alignment at front and sides.

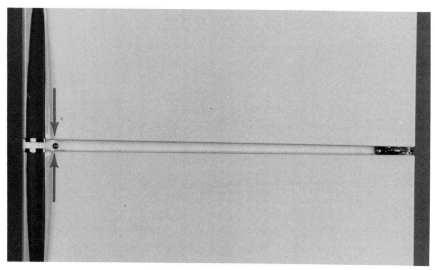

Door out of alignment

Step 1: UNPLUG the refrigerator or freezer from the wall receptacle. Watch for sharp edges.

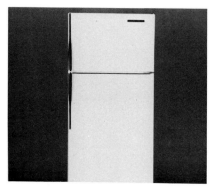

Step 2: Make sure refrigerator or freezer cabinet is level side to side. Refrigerator and upright freezer cabinets should be tilted slightly to the rear to allow the door to close itself.

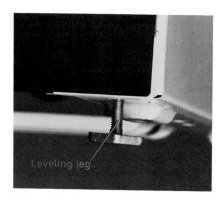

Step 3: Leveling legs permit adjustments to the refrigerator or freezer. Turn the leveling legs clockwise to raise appliance, counterclockwise to lower. Be sure legs are set so appliance is firmly positioned on the floor.

Door alignment (continued)

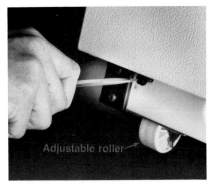

Step 4: Adjustable rollers are located behind grille. To remove grille, please refer to Procedure #7: Condenser Cleaning. Turn roller, adjusting screws clockwise to raise cabinet. Be sure appliance is firmly positioned on floor.

Step 5: Door can be moved in or out by making adjustments on the hinges. Hinges with elongated holes permit adjustment at top of door. Center and bottom hinges adjust by adding or removing shims from behind the hinge.

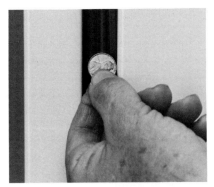

Step 6: If spacing appears to be uneven on hinge side of door, a penny or dime can be used to check for consistency along the gasket seal of your appliance. Check fit top to bottom. Make adjustments if necessary.

Step 7: If the door is out of plane from the front or handle side, adjustment can be made by loosening all screws holding the inner door panel. Note: Failure to loosen all screws may result in cracked inner door panel.

Step 8: Pull section of door that appears to be out of plane. Hold door rigid; tighten screws at corners of inner door panel. Repeat if necessary. After door is properly aligned, tighten all screws.

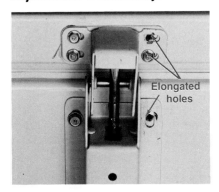

Elongated holes

Step 9: Lid adjustment on chest freezers can be made at hinges. Elongated holes in hinges allow for horizontal or vertical adjustment. Loosen screws, move lid into proper alignment. Tighten screws.

Step 10: CAUTION: Lid hinges are mounted under spring pressure. Hold hinge while removing screws. Gradually release pressure when screws are removed. (Take extreme care when making adjustments or removing lid on chest freezers).

Step 11: On chest freezer, check plane of lid at rear. If corner is not sealing, loosen screws in lower portion of both hinges. Make adjustment and then tighten screws while lid is aligned to cabinet.

Step 12: Reassemble refrigerator or freezer and reconnect power supply.

Procedure 12
Inspecting and replacing door gaskets

Skill Level Rating: | Easy | Average | **Difficult** | Very Difficult

A door gasket that does not seal properly will allow entry of warm, moisture-laden air which will quickly form frost on the evaporator and increase compressor running time. Therefore, door gaskets should be checked as an energy conservation measure.

Occasionally, use of a dollar bill is recommended for checking the door gasket seal. The technique was developed many years ago when refrigerators had mechanical door latches and firm rubber door gaskets. The latch mechanism applied the necessary pressure to hold the door firmly closed and the gasket tightly sealed. If the dollar bill was held tightly by the gasket, and could not be pulled free without fear of tearing the paper, this was proof that the gasket was sealing properly.

Most refrigerators in use today do not have mechanical door latches. A federal regulation to prevent child entrapment requires the force necessary to open a refrigerator or freezer door from within must not exceed 15 pounds. Thus with the lower sealing pressure of gaskets used on modern refrigerators, a dollar bill can be easily pulled free from between the gasket and cabinet face--even though the gasket is sealing satisfactorily.

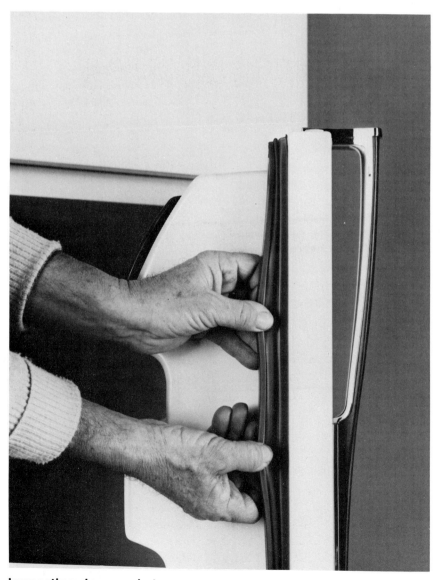

Inspecting door gasket

Door gaskets (continued)

Step 1: UNPLUG the refrigerator or freezer from the wall receptacle. Watch for sharp edges.

Step 2: Be sure gasket replacement is absolutely necessary. Incorrect door alignment can cause poor gasket sealing. Re-leveling cabinet or adjustment to hinge may correct seal. Read Procedure #11: Door Alignment.

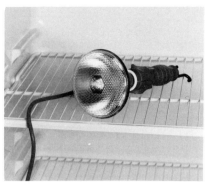

Step 3: The only sure method of checking a door gasket seal is to place a 150 watt outdoor flood light inside the cabinet. Do not use an indoor lamp. Direct light at one length of gasket at a time with door closed. Gasket will allow door to close on cord.

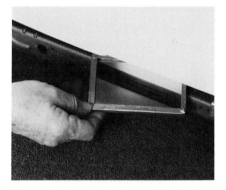

Step 4: Inspect at seal for light translucency; use mirror to inspect along length of gasket at bottom of door. A satisfactory seal is present when there is no light leakage. Any visible damage calls for a new gasket.

Step 5: There are three basic types of door gaskets: compression, magnetic or a combination of both. Compression type gaskets are used on chest freezers and on refrigerators that have a magnetic door latch.

Step 6: Most magnetic gaskets have magnetic strips at all four sides. Some are designed to have less pull on hinge side of cabinet. The weaker magnetic side is identified by ribs or a small hole on underside of gasket.

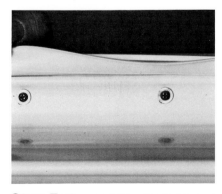

Step 7: On models where screws pass through inner door panel and gasket, it is sometimes necessary to remove screws. Make note of gasket installation and screws used for reference and replacement.

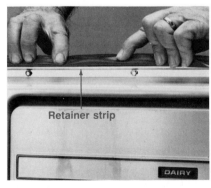

Retainer strip

Step 8: To remove a gasket in models having retainer strips, it is only necessary to loosen screws that pass through retainer and inner door panel. Gasket can then be pulled free from under retainer.

Step 9: To replace gasket, loosen or remove screws for top two-thirds of door liner. Take old gasket out; install new gasket. Make sure lip of gasket is fully under edge of retainer strip. Do not tighten screws completely.

Door gaskets (continued)

Step 10: Complete lower third of door gasket. Adjust door alignment with cabinet before tightening screws. If you are unfamiliar with this process, please refer to Procedure #11: Door Alignment.

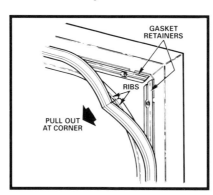

GASKET RETAINERS

RIBS

PULL OUT AT CORNER

Step 11: Other door gaskets press fit into retainers at all four sides of each inner door. To remove gasket, grasp at one corner, and pull from retainers.

Step 12: To ease installation, rub paraffin into retainer groove. Place gasket on door and position rib of gasket in retainer groove. Start at one corner and press gasket at 1″ intervals to firmly seat rib into retainer.

Step 13: After gasket is installed, rub a thin film of pure paraffin wax on hinge side of gasket sealing surface. Apply one or two coats of wax uniformly from top to bottom to provide lubrication.

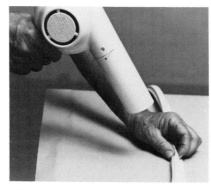

Step 14: Compression gaskets may take time to seat properly. If new gasket has wrinkles or creases when removed from carton, use a hair dryer or warm water to soften gasket and remove wrinkles.

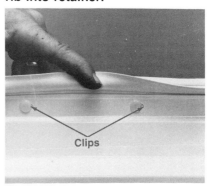

Clips

Step 15: Compression type gaskets are generally used on chest freezers. Some have a magnetic strip at handle side of lid. Clips and/or plastic pins are used to hold gasket and inner panel to lid.

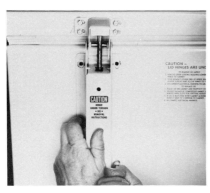

Step 16: To replace chest freezer gasket, remove lid. CAUTION: Use extreme care when removing freezer hinges. Hinges are mounted with spring pressure. Hold tension on hinge while removing screws, gradually release pressure when screws are removed.

Step 17: Place lid upside down on quilt over freezer cabinet. This will make gasket easier to replace and quilt will protect cabinet finish. (May require two people).

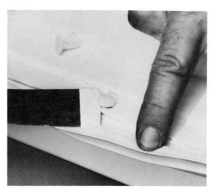

Step 18: To remove gasket, carefully pry out clips. Wrap putty knife blade with masking tape so as not to damage inner liner or break clips.

Door gaskets (continued)

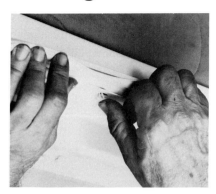

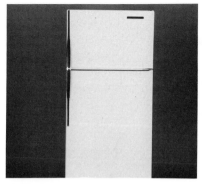

Step 19: Take note of how retaining clips are installed for new gasket replacement. To replace chest freezer gasket, fit new gasket beneath inner panel and reinsert clips, working gasket carefully in place.

Step 20: Lids on chest freezers are designed to "float" and self align. Make adjustments for lid alignment at hinges. If you are unfamiliar with this process, refer to Procedure #11: Door Alignment.

Step 21: Reassemble refrigerator and reconnect power supply.

Procedure 13
Cosmetic repairs

Skill Level Rating:	Easy	**Average**	Difficult	Very Difficult

You can help keep the appearance of your refrigerator or freezer in "showroom" condition by following the maintenance instructions in your *Use and Care Book* or in the preventive maintenance section of this manual. Properly applying a coat of appliance polish wax at least twice a year will help your appliance maintain a new look and provide protection against rust.

However, over the years through accidents or moving, you may encounter problems that involve more extensive cosmetic repairs. Handles, nameplates, trim and the like can usually be replaced. Painted cabinet bodies can be touched up with spray paint or touch up pencils. These products are usually available through your local authorized appliance parts dealer.

Note: Be sure to use the correct model identification number when purchasing paint.

CAUTION: Paint is flammable. Always paint in well ventilated area away from open flame. Read all cautions on paint container. Do not spray paint on the front flange of refrigerator near the gasket seal. Vinyl gaskets react chemically with most paints and paint will become soft and sticky.

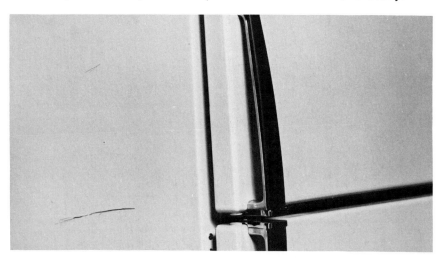

Matching touch up paint is available for repairing scratches

Step 1: UNPLUG the refrigerator or freezer from the wall receptacle. Paint is flammable. Spray in well ventilated area.

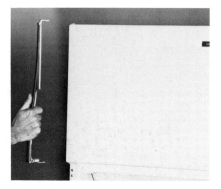

Step 2: Damaged trim is replaced by removing retaining screws or clips. When removing trim, take precautions against chipping or scratching finish.

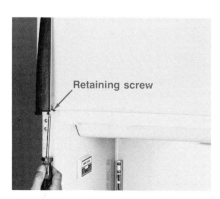

Step 3: To avoid chipping use care not to overtighten screws that attach trim to painted or porcelain finish. When using a putty knife to pry trim, wrap blade with masking tape to prevent accidental scratching.

45

Cosmetic repairs (continued)

Step 4: To remove soil, wash cabinet with a liquid household detergent. Remove all traces of wax with a wax remover. Rinse with clear water and dry with clean cloth.

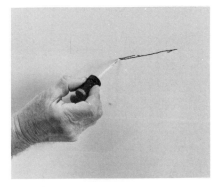

Step 5: To repair small scratches, spray small amount of paint into top of can and dip torn match in paint or use touch up paint with brush applicator. Use paint sparingly to fill scratch.

Step 6: Large scratches with deep edges should be sanded. Sand until edge is feathered. Final sanding should be with extra fine sandpaper for smooth finish.

Step 7: Tape newspaper around sanded area and around any chrome to protect against overspray. Use primer coat first. Light primer is used for light colors, gray for dark colors.

Step 8: Practice with spray can before applying paint to appliance. Read and follow instructions on paint can. Do not aim paint spray directly at damaged area.

Step 9: Tear an irregular hole in a piece of paper. Spray damaged area through this hole. This allows paint to blend with original coat without obvious lines. Do not apply too much paint as it will run and sag.

Step 10: After primer has dried, sand lightly and spray with matching appliance finish coat. Be sure to read instructions on can carefully.

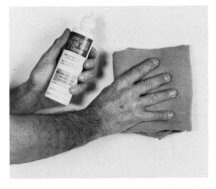

Step 11: Allow finish coat to dry and re-wax with appliance polish wax. Be careful not to allow wax or paint to come in contact with door gaskets or plastic surfaces.

Procedure 14
Inspecting and replacing light and fan switches

Skill Level Rating: | Easy | Average | **Difficult** | Very Difficult

Interior light and fan switches are usually mounted so they are directly operated by the door. When the door is opened, the light inside your refrigerator comes on. A closed door activates the fan motor switch. Some refrigerators and freezers have separate switches to activate the fan and light. Other models have a dual purpose switch which is a combination light and fan switch.

While interior lights are certainly considered a "necessary" convenience, the evaporator fan plays a more vital part in cooling your refrigerator. The evaporator fan circulates air throughout the freezer and fresh food compartments. Faulty operation of either of these switches (light remains on--fan remains off) can be a source of poor refrigeration.

Door-operated switches are either plunger type or rocker type. Both types of switches are used on refrigerators and freezers. Inspection and replacement procedures are basically the same.

Note: If you suspect the interior light remains on inside the refrigerator or freezer when the door is closed, look into the compartment while opening the door slowly. If the switch turns off when it is manually operated, but remains on when door is closed, the problem may be with door alignment. To make necessary adjustment, please refer to Procedure #11: Door Alignment.

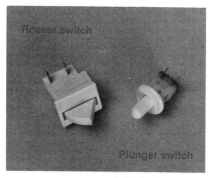

Plunger and rocker switches

Step 1: UNPLUG the refrigerator or freezer from the wall receptacle. Watch for sharp edges behind breaker strips.

Step 2: This procedure requires the use of an ohmmeter. For instructions, please refer to Tools and Testing Equipment, page 98.

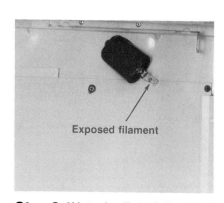

Exposed filament

Step 3: If interior light fails, check bulb by using another bulb of same size and wattage. Use same size bulb as original to prevent overheating plastic shield. To prevent cuts from glass breakage, use extreme care when removing bulb. Wear protective gloves or use pliers if bulb is broken.

Light and fan switches (continued)

Step 4: If switch is mounted on breaker strip, breaker must be removed for access. If you are unfamiliar with this process, please refer to Procedure #8: Breaker Strips.

Step 5: Remove rocker type switch by using a putty knife with a tape wrapped blade. Pry out the left side of switch slightly, then pry right side out fully.

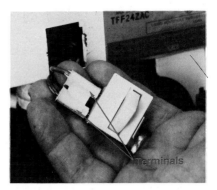

Step 6: Unplug switch from molded plug. Visually inspect switch for damage such as corroded or damaged terminals.

Step 7: If there is no visible damage, check switch with ohmmeter. Set ohmmeter to R x 1 position. For light switch, needle should sweep upscale to zero. Depress plunger, needle should not move.

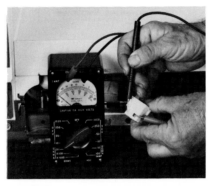

Step 8: To test fan switch, set ohmmeter to R x 1. Needle should not move. When plunger is depressed, needle should sweep upscale to zero.

Step 9: Be sure to replace faulty switch with correct replacement part. Attach connectors and replace switch in mounting. Check operation of switch by slowly opening and closing door.

Step 10: Some replacement switches for older models are supplied with an adapter plate and two lead wires. It may be necessary to enlarge mounting hole in breaker strip to accept replacement switch.

Step 11: If hole in breaker strip is larger than switch body, position adapter plate over the backside of switch to secure it to breaker strip.

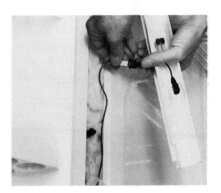

Step 12: Adapter lead wires are used to connect the wiring harness to new switch if the terminals on the new switch are a smaller size than on the original switch. Reassemble appliance and reconnect power supply.

Procedure 15
Testing and replacing condenser fan motor

Skill Level Rating: | Easy | Average | **Difficult** | Very Difficult |

Only refrigerators and freezers that have condensers located in the machine compartment have a fan to circulate room air over the condenser and compressor. The room air enters the machine compartment through the front grille located at the base of the cabinet. It then circulates over and through the condenser, picking up heat.

On these models, warm air is discharged over the drain pan, and expelled through the front grille at the left side. On some side by side models, the fan discharges air over the compressor and expels the air at the rear of the cabinet. The condenser fan provides a secondary benefit to these models by aiding evaporation of water in the drain pan.

Note: Be sure appliance cabinet is not elevated above the floor to the extent the baffles on underside of machine compartment are ineffective, allowing air flow to bypass the condenser.

Condenser fan

Step 1: UNPLUG the refrigerator or freezer from the wall receptacle. Watch for sharp edges inside machine compartment.

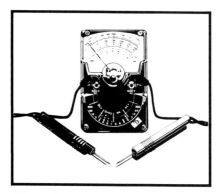

Step 2: This procedure requires the use of an ohmmeter. For instructions, please refer to Tools and Testing Equipment, page 98.

Step 3: This procedure requires the removal of the access panel from your refrigerator or freezer. If you are unfamiliar with this process, please refer to Procedure #3: Removing Access Panels.

Step 4: In time the condenser will collect lint and dust, impeding air flow. Clean condenser periodically. If you are unfamiliar with this process, please refer to Procedure #7: Condenser Cleaning.

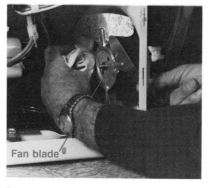

Fan blade

Step 5: Check fan blade. If there is accumulated dust, clean blade to improve efficiency of fan. Be sure wiring is connected to fan motor after cleaning blade.

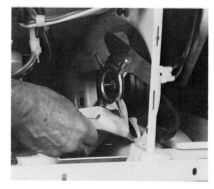

Step 6: Check for obstructions around fan blade. Condenser fan motor can stall due to obstructions of blade. After removing obstruction, it should not be necessary to replace motor. Motor is designed to withstand prolonged stall.

Condenser fan motor (continued)

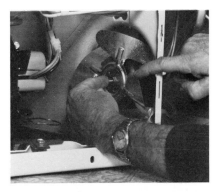

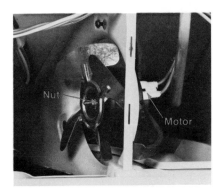

Step 7: Rotate fan blade slowly by hand to check for any internal motor binding. Spin fan blade briskly. It should spin freely. If fan is sluggish or stops abruptly, there is internal binding.

Step 8: If motor binds or bearings were noisy when appliance was operating, replace motor. If blade is distorted, replace blade. Blade can be replaced without removing motor (see Step 12).

Step 9: To check fan motor, remove push-on connectors. Set ohmmeter to R x 1 scale. Place probes on terminals of fan motor. If ohmmeter needle does not move, replace fan motor.

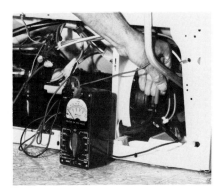

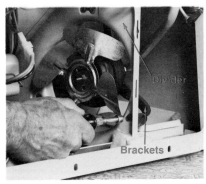

Step 10: To check fan motor to ground, set ohmmeter to R x 1000 or higher. Touch one probe to terminal, the other to case. Repeat on other terminal. Ohmmeter needle should not move. If either test fails, replace motor.

Step 11: To remove fan assembly, remove bracket screws fastening fan to metal divider in machine compartment. Then remove screws fastening fan to brackets. Make note of position of blade on shaft.

Step 12: Remove nut securing fan blade to shaft of motor. Reinstall rubber washer, blade and nut on shaft of new motor. Remount fan assembly to divider in machine compartment.

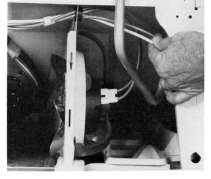

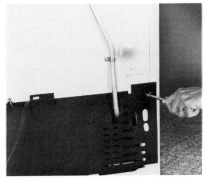

Step 13: When divider has key hole slots to aid in mounting bracket, be sure screw heads do not "crawl" out of slots while tightening mounting screws. Reinstall wiring connections.

Step 14: Arrange wiring so wires do not obstruct fan blades in any way. Make sure all screws are tight to prevent unnecessary noise.

Step 15: Reassemble refrigerator or freezer and reconnect power supply.

Procedure 16
Inspecting and replacing temperature control

Skill Level Rating:	Easy	Average	Difficult	**Very Difficult**

A temperature control is used on all refrigerators and freezers to regulate the operation of the compressor and thus maintain desired food temperatures. The temperature control knob usually has numbered settings and an OFF setting. Some freezer models do not have an OFF setting to prevent the freezer from inadvertently being turned off.

The temperature control consists primarily of a capillary tube and bellows assembly, a set of normally closed contacts, and a mechanical linkage. Pressure within the gas-charged capillary tube and bellows assembly responds to temperature along the length of the capillary tube. The bellows assembly actuates the linkage and allows the contacts to open or close.

On some models, the control senses evaporator temperature and, on others, the temperature of the air. Accordingly, a control that has the capillary tube fastened to the evaporator is calibrated to a much colder temperature than one that has the capillary tube suspended in the air stream.

Note: Some models will have a plastic sleeve positioned over capillary. When replacing temperature control, transfer sleeve from inoperative control to replacement.

Note: Capillary tube is connected to control assembly. There are several methods of attaching capillary tube to refrigerator. Make careful note of capillary tube on your model.

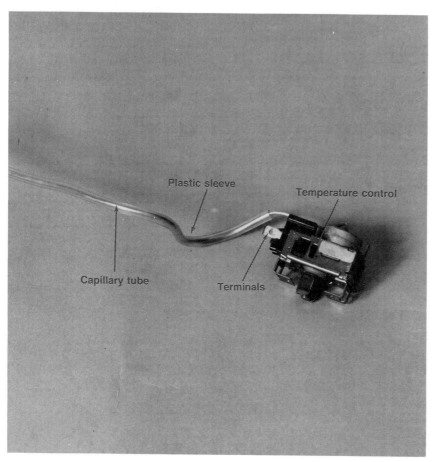

Temperature control assembly

Temperature control (continued)

Step 1: UNPLUG refrigerator or freezer from the wall receptacle. Watch for sharp edges on inner liner.

Step 2: This procedure requires the use of an ohmmeter. For instructions, please refer to Tools and Testing Equipment page 98.

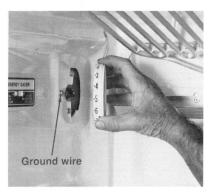

Ground wire

Step 3: To remove temperature control on most models, pull control knob straight off. Remove screws, and remove control from opening. Disconnect push-on leads and ground wire.

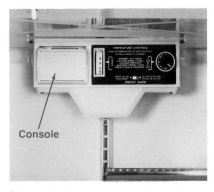

Console

Step 4: Other models have the temperature control covered by a temperature control console. Remove console screws and release from inner cabinet. Make note of installation for reference when reassembling.

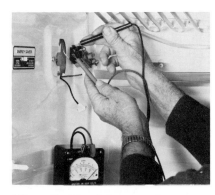

Step 5: Check temperature control for continuity. Set ohmmeter on R x 1 setting. Place one probe on each terminal. When control is turned to "ON", ohmmeter needle should sweep upscale to zero.

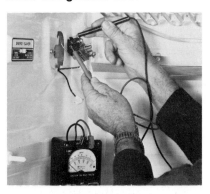

Step 6: Repeat test with control in "OFF" position. Ohmmeter needle should not move. If control fails either test, replace control.

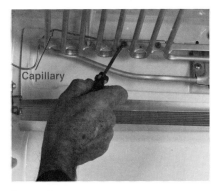

Capillary

Step 7: The capillary tube is part of the temperature control assembly. Make note of capillary tube placement. There are several methods of attaching capillary, and it is extremely important to install capillary in its original position.

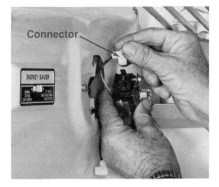

Connector

Step 8: To replace control, firmly push connectors onto control. Reattach ground wire to original location.

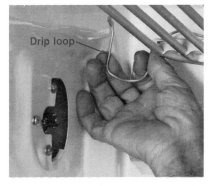

Drip loop

Step 9: On models with capillary attached to evaporator, route tube behind liner, out opening near evaporator. Insert into clamp and fasten clamp screws tightly. Drip loop should be formed in capillary tube.

Temperature control (continued)

Step 10: On models with capillary wrapped around thermal mass, as shown, loosen or remove thermal mass. Remove old control and capillary. Wind new capillary around thermal mass tightly.

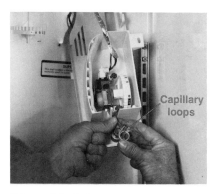

Step 11: Slip new capillary off thermal mass. Reduce coil diameter of loops by twisting capillary. Insert thermal mass back into loops with rotating motion. Reinstall control and thermal mass with capillary in position.

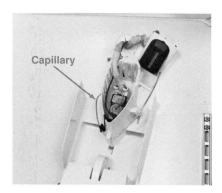

Step 12: If capillary is suspended in air, take careful note of installation. Some capillary tubes are coiled inside control console, others are positioned outside console. Reinstall in original position.

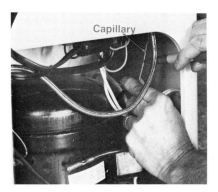

Step 13: When capillary is inserted in a well, first mark old tube at point it enters well. After removing control, mark new capillary tube at same point.

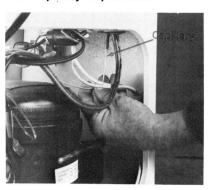

Step 14: Insert new capillary tube into well to mark. Seal capillary well opening with permagum. This prevents condensation from dripping from well.

Step 15: Reassemble refrigerator or freezer and reconnect power supply.

Notes

Procedure 17
Removing evaporator covers

For reasons of safety and appearance, the evaporator and other components are concealed behind the evaporator cover.

In automatic defrost refrigerators and freezers, the evaporator is located behind a rear panel or the freezer floor cover. These models use a fan to circulate cold air within the food compartments and over the evaporator. In order to make repairs to the fan or other evaporator related components, the evaporator cover must be removed.

In non-automatic defrost refrigerators, the evaporator is literally the freezer compartment. Frost is visible on surfaces of the freezer compartment. The food stored inside is cooled by natural convection air currents. Cycle defrost models have a second evaporator or "cooling coil" located at the top of the fresh food compartment.

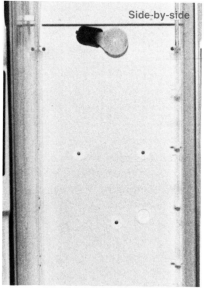

Side-by-side, rear wall evaporator cover

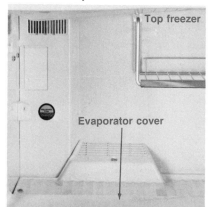

Top freezer floor evaporator cover

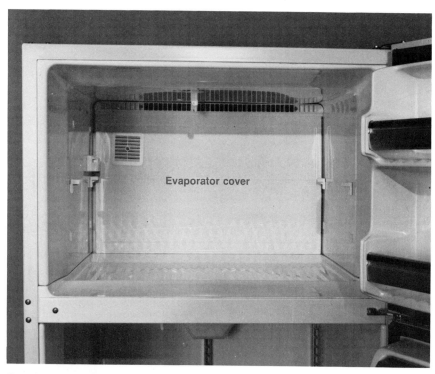

Top freezer, rear wall evaporator cover

Step 1: UNPLUG the refrigerator or freezer from the wall receptacle. Watch for sharp edges behind evaporator cover.

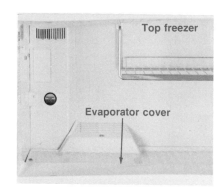

Step 2: Remove all food and shelving from freezer compartment. Make a careful visual inspection of freezer compartment to determine location of evaporator (rear wall or freezer floor).

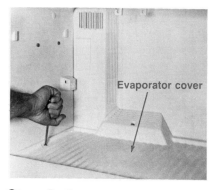

Step 3: Evaporator beneath freezer floor. Remove all screws from freezer floor. Remove ducts and grilles as necessary. For installation reference make note of how screws are removed.

Evaporator covers (continued)

Step 4: Grasp freezer floor at rear. Raise freezer floor from back while disengaging floor at front. Pull freezer floor up and out.

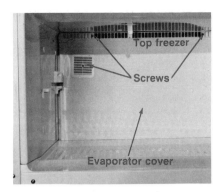

Step 5: Evaporator behind back wall. Some top mount freezer/refrigerator models have evaporator located behind back wall. Make a visual inspection of screws and grilles.

Step 6: Remove all screws and grilles, as necessary. Note and remove ground screw (ground wire connection).

Step 7: To remove back wall evaporator cover, pull cover at an angle. Handle cover carefully to prevent scratching or damage to freezer floor or liner surface.

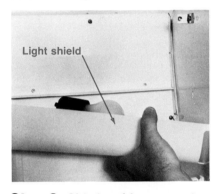

Step 8: Side-by-side evaporator cover. Before removing evaporator cover, remove light shield and bulb if covering screw heads.

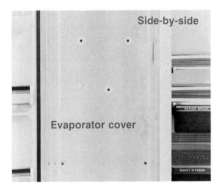

Step 9: Remove all screws, making note of position for reinstallation reference. Top center screw is ground screw.

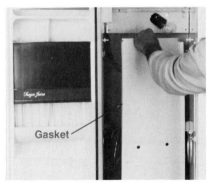

Step 10: Tilt evaporator cover forward to remove. As cover is removed, gaskets will usually come out also. **Note:** On some models, light socket may first need to be removed prior to cover removal. Take note of gasket fit and use care not to damage gasket.

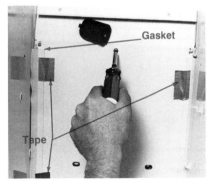

Step 11: When replacing side-by-side evaporator cover, it may be necessary to tape gasket temporarily in place with masking tape to front of cover. Replace cover, starting with ground screw. After cover is secured, remove tape.

Step 12: After completing any repairs, reassemble refrigerator or freezer. Replace ground screw. Reconnect power supply.

Inspecting and replacing evaporator fan

Skill Level Rating:	Easy	Average	Difficult	**Very Difficult**

An evaporator fan is used on automatic defrost refrigerators and freezers. Cold air from the evaporator is drawn through the fan and discharged into the freezer and fresh food compartments. The air circulates through both compartments, picking up heat from the food stored inside. Warmer air is then returned through the evaporator.

The evaporator fan is located in the freezer compartment. It is usually concealed behind the evaporator cover and/or other grilles or covers.

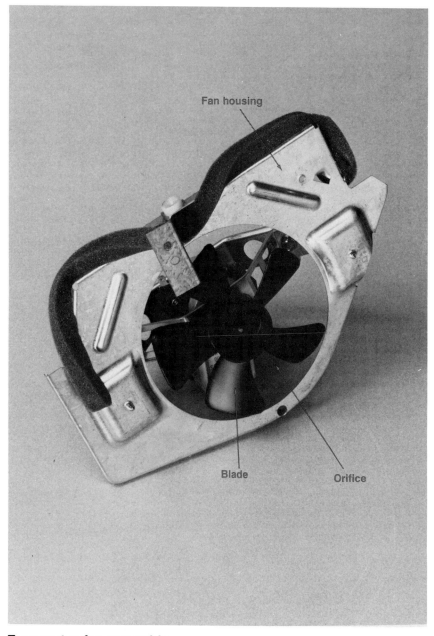

Evaporator fan assembly

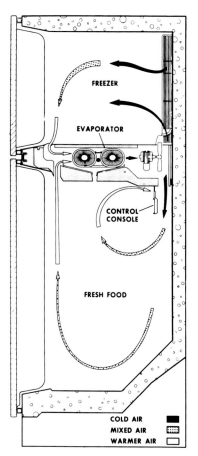

Top mount design

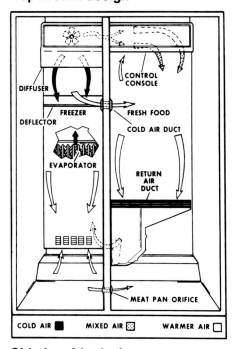

Side-by-side design

Evaporator fan (continued)

Step 1: UNPLUG the refrigerator or freezer from the wall receptacle. Watch for sharp edges.

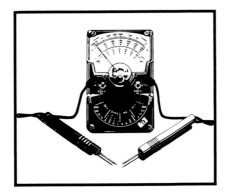

Step 2: This procedure requires the use of an ohmmeter. For instructions, please refer to Tools and Testing Equipment, page 98.

Step 3: This procedure may require the removal of evaporator cover. If you are unfamiliar with this process, please refer to Procedure #17: Removing Evaporator Covers.

Step 4: After removing evaporator cover, the evaporator fan will be visible. Take note of how fan is positioned and wires are routed for future installation reference.

Step 5: Visually inspect for any obstructions. Fan motor can stall due to an obstruction of the fan blade. Fan motors are designed to withstand prolonged stalled conditions without damage.

Step 6: On some models fan assembly can be lifted out. This allows for easy access to mounting screws after removing bracket retainer screw.

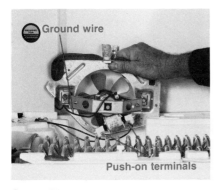

Step 7: Motor mounting bracket screws at each side of motor must be removed from fan housing to free motor. Disconnect ground wire and remove push-on terminals from motor. Remove fan motor from appliance to test.

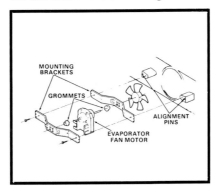

Step 8: On some models, two identical brackets are used to mount fan motor to fan housing. Unscrew mounting brackets from fan housing. Use care to avoid bending brackets.

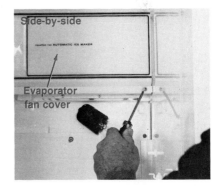

Step 9: Side-by-side. Most side-by-side models require only the removal of a fan cover to gain access to evaporator fan motor. Generally, two screws are used to secure fan cover.

Evaporator fan (continued)

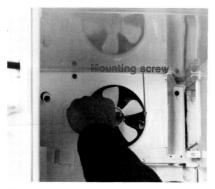

Step 10: To remove motor, first remove the mounting screws behind fan blade. As fan is removed, be careful to avoid dropping rubber grommet at rear of motor.

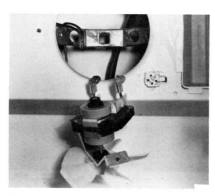

Step 11: Remove push-on connectors and ground wire, making note of wire configuration for reinstallation.

Step 12: Fan motor can now be tested. All evaporator fan motors are tested by the same methods. Avoid losing rubber grommet while testing motor.

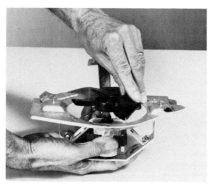

Step 13: To check for internal binding, spin the fan blade (in either direction) by hand with fan motor assembly positioned up and a second time with assembly positioned down. The fan should spin freely.

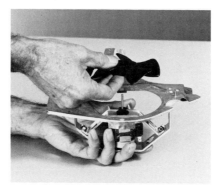

Step 14: If the fan motor binds, or if the bearings were noisy when the appliance was operating, replace motor. If blade is broken or loose on shaft, replace blade. (See Step 15).

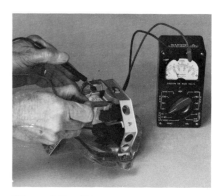

Step 15: Check the fan motor winding with an ohmmeter. Set ohmmeter to R × 1 scale. Place probes on terminals. If needle does not move, replace fan motor.

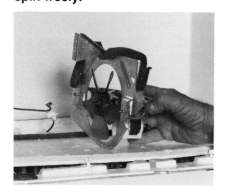

Step 16: To replace fan motor or fan blade, make note how blade is positioned on shaft.

Step 17: Mark blade with marker pen for installation reference. Note position of compression ring at end of motor shaft. To remove fan blade, pull blade straight off shaft.

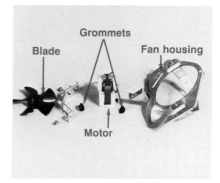

Step 18: Use replacement motor of same size and capacity. Reassemble fan assembly. Be sure to position fan blade correctly. If blade is not properly positioned or is reversed, fan will not properly propel air.

Evaporator fan (continued)

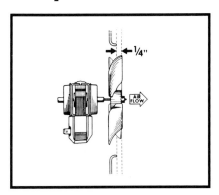

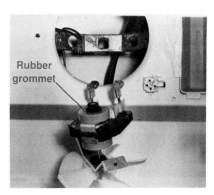

Step 19: Usually the fan blade should be installed on the shaft so that ¾ of its depth (or approximately ¼ inch) protrudes through the fan orifice in the direction of the air flow.

Step 20: For top mount refrigerator, reinstall fan, making sure all brackets and screws are firmly in place. Arrange wires so they do not obstruct fan blade. Attach ground wires and push-on connectors. Reinstall evaporator cover.

Step 21: For side-by-side refrigerator, replace fan assembly and reconnect all push-on connectors and ground wire. Replace fan assembly mounting bracket inside fan orifice. Make sure rubber grommet is positioned over post at the rear of the motor.

Step 22: Reinstall evaporator cover or fan cover. Reassemble appliance and reconnect power supply.

Procedure 19
Inspecting and replacing defrost control

Skill Level Rating: | Easy | Average | Difficult | **Very Difficult** |

All automatic defrost refrigerators and freezers have a defrost control to melt accumulated frost from the evaporator. The defrost control acts as a timer to regulate the frequency of the defrost cycle and the duration of each cycle.

The defrost control consists of a timer motor, a gear assembly, a switch, and a rotating cam. The frequency of the defrost cycle can be 6 to 12 hours with the duration of the cycle being 20 to 35 minutes. After about 6 to 12 hours of control motor run time, the cam rotates to a point where it operates the switch contacts. This interrupts power to the compressor and energizes the defrost heater(s).

Note: Failure of a defrost control usually results in a frost-blocked evaporator. Remove all frost or ice completely to prevent a residual icing condition. Exercise care if using a heat gun or hair dryer to prevent melting any adjacent plastic or foam parts.

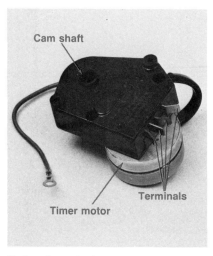

Defrost control

Step 1: UNPLUG the refrigerator or freezer from the wall receptacle. Watch for sharp edges in machine compartment.

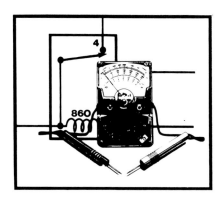

Step 2: This procedure requires the use of an ohmmeter and the ability to read a circuit diagram. For instructions, please refer to Tools and Testing Equipment, pages 98-100.

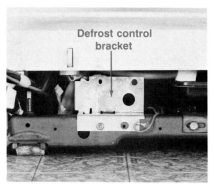

Step 3: The defrost control is usually located behind the grille at the bottom of the cabinet. If you are unfamiliar with removing the grille, please refer to Procedure #7: Condenser Cleaning.

Step 4: Some freezer models have the defrost control located in the machine compartment. Servicing this type of control may require removal of the access panel. If you are unfamiliar with this process, please refer to Procedure #3: Access Panels.

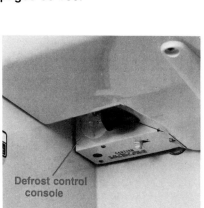

Step 5: The defrost control in some refrigerators is located behind a console in the top of the fresh food compartment. Remove food and shelves to access control. Remove screws that hold console in place.

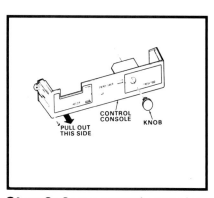

Step 6: Some control consoles have only one screw at left. Remove temperature control knob, screw, and pull outward from left side.

Defrost control (continued)

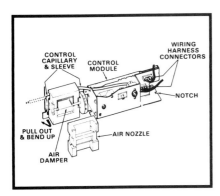

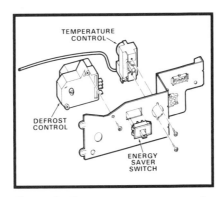

Step 7: To remove control module, disconnect push-on connectors, making note of proper connections. Pull end of control capillary and sleeve from channel. Bend capillary to horizontal position.

Step 8: Remove screws securing control module to liner. Pull assembly out leaving capillary sleeve in place behind air damper foam housing. Reinstall in reverse order, making certain capillary is fully inserted into sleeve before mounting assembly.

Step 9: Look closely at the defrost control. Control terminals are numbered. Numbers correspond with switches and contacts within the defrost control assembly. The cam has a slot or knob so it may be turned manually.

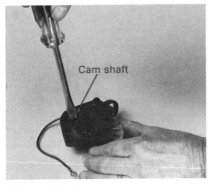

Step 10: Turn cam clockwise by inserting a screwdriver in cam shaft slot. Turn slowly until you hear an audible snap. This sound occurs at the beginning and end of each defrost cycle.

Step 11: Align mark on cam shaft with mark on case of defrost control. One snap should be heard. Set ohmmeter to R × 1 scale. Place probes on terminals 2 and 3. Needle should sweep to zero. If needle does not move, replace control.

Step 12: Advance cam until second snap is heard. Place ohmmeter probes on terminals 3 and 4. Needle should sweep upscale to zero. If needle does not move, replace control.

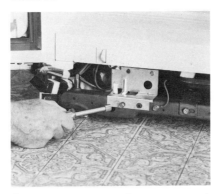

Step 13: Set ohmmeter to R × 100 scale. Place probes on terminals 3 and 1 to check motor resistance. Meter should read approximately 800-3200 ohms. If not, replace control.

Step 14: To install new control, position connectors on proper terminals. Position control, secure to bracket, and bracket to mounting location. Attach ground wire. Reassemble appliance and reconnect power supply.

Procedure 20

Inspecting and replacing defrost thermostat

Skill Level Rating: | Easy | Average | Difficult | **Very Difficult** |

The defrost thermostat is used to de-energize the defrost heater after frost has melted from the evaporator during the defrost cycle. When all the frost has been completely removed from the evaporator, the temperature of the evaporator begins to rise rapidly. When the limit temperature of the thermostat is sensed, a bimetal disk inside the thermostat warps and causes the thermostat contacts to open. When the temperature of the evaporator has cooled sufficiently, the bimetal disk warps in the opposite direction, closing the contacts.

CAUTION: The defrost thermostat is an important part of the defrost system of a refrigerator or freezer. It should never be by-passed in the circuit. Bypassing the thermostat could cause overheating of the defrost heater(s) and surrounding surfaces, which could result in severe damage to the appliance.

Note: Test defrost thermostat while thermostat is mounted in refrigerator. If thermostat is warm, contacts will be open, giving a false reading.

Note: A defective thermostat usually results in a frost-blocked evaporator. Remove all frost or ice completely to prevent a residual icing condition. Exercise care if using a heat gun or hair dryer to prevent melting any adjacent plastic or foam parts.

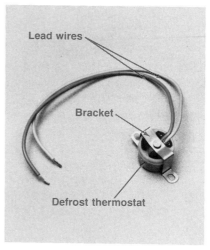

Defrost thermostat

Step 1: UNPLUG the refrigerator or freezer from the wall receptacle. Watch for sharp edges on evaporator.

Step 2: This procedure requires the use of an ohmmeter. For instructions, please refer to Tools and Testing Equipment, page 98.

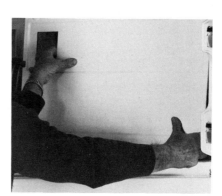

Step 3: This procedure requires the removal of the evaporator cover. If you are unfamiliar with this process, please refer to Procedure #17: Removing Evaporator Covers.

Defrost thermostat (continued)

Step 4: Defrost thermostats are mounted in various locations. On some models, thermostat is mounted on a metal drain pan or plate.

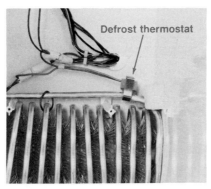

Step 5: On side-by-side models, defrost thermostat is mounted directly to evaporator tubing at top of evaporator.

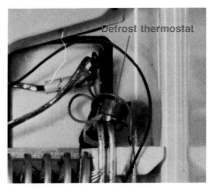

Step 6: To correctly test thermostat, it must be mounted in a cold refrigerator. If thermostat is warm, contacts will be open, giving a false reading.

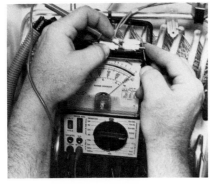

Step 7: To test thermostat with push-on connectors, set ohmmeter to R × 1 scale. Remove connectors and touch probes to terminals. Needle should sweep to zero.

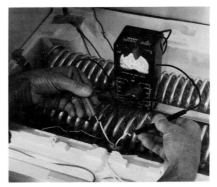

Step 8: To test thermostat without push-on connectors, cut lead wires 3″ to 4″ from thermostat, but leave in refrigerator. Set ohmmeter to R × 1 scale. Touch probes to bare wires. Needle should sweep zero.

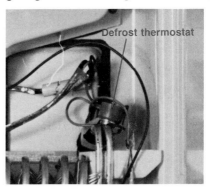

Step 9: If defrost thermostat is cold and ohmmeter test indicates no continuity, defrost thermostat must be replaced. If thermostat checks good, splice wires as in Steps 10-12.

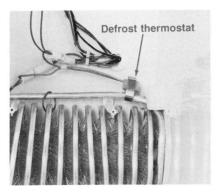

Step 10: Replacement thermostat must be spliced to lead wires in all models. Cut wires to push-on connectors, if necessary.

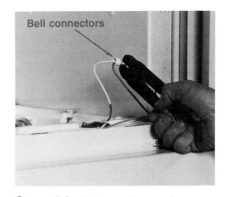

Step 11: Make splice and cover splice with bell connectors. If you are unfamiliar with this process, refer to Procedure #4: Wiring and Connections.

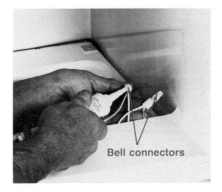

Step 12: IMPORTANT: Fill open ends of bell connectors with RTV silicone sealer (FDA approved only) to prevent moisture from entering connection. Reassemble appliance and reconnect power supply.

Procedure 21
Inspecting and replacing defrost heaters

Skill Level Rating: | Easy | Average | Difficult | **Very Difficult** |

Automatic defrost model refrigerators have one or more heaters to melt the frost that has accumulated on the evaporator during compressor running cycle. Most models have radiant type defrost heaters. The heater element is enclosed in a glass tube with push-on terminals in the end cap insulators. Most models use only a single heater. Other models use either two or three heaters. When one heater in a series has failed, all heaters should be replaced as a complete set. Replacement of only one heater will cause early failure of other heater(s).

Single heaters are furnished as identical replacements. On models where more than one heater is used, a complete set of heaters is supplied as a kit which contains a jumper wire and alternate reflector shield. Install the replacement heater assembly without modification. The alternate shields are to be used if the original heater does not have an attached rear reflector shield as shown.

Note: Failure of a defrost heater usually results in a frost blocked evaporator. Remove all frost or ice completely to prevent a residual icing condition. Exercise care if using a heat gun or hair dryer to prevent melting any adjacent plastic or foam parts.

Defrost heater for top mount models

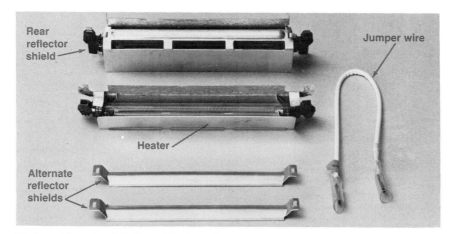

Defrost heater kit for side-by-side models

Step 1: UNPLUG the refrigerator or freezer from wall receptacle. Watch for sharp edges on the evaporator.

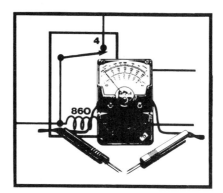

Step 2: This procedure requires the use of an ohmmeter and the ability to read a circuit diagram. For instructions, please refer to **Tools and Testing Equipment, pages 98-100.**

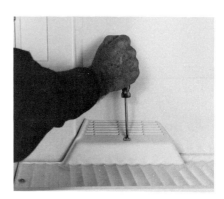

Step 3: This procedure requires the removal of the evaporator cover to gain access to defrost heater(s). If you are unfamiliar with this process, please refer to **Procedure #l7: Removing Evaporator Covers.**

Defrost heaters (continued)

Step 4: Some side-by-side models have heaters mounted behind a reflector shield assembly.

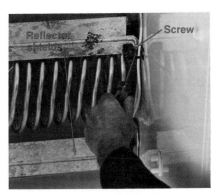

Step 5: To remove heater assemblies of this type, remove screw at each end of reflector to detach from evaporator.

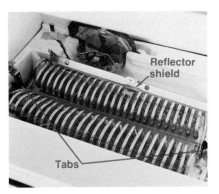

Step 6: Some defrost heaters are installed as single units and without attached reflectors. To remove heater(s), detach push-on connectors. Bend tabs at end of heater brackets and remove separate reflector shield.

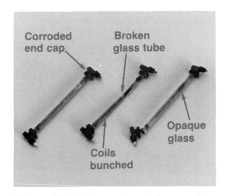

Step 7: Make a visual inspection of the defrost heater. Check for broken glass tube, opaque glass, element coils bunched together, or broken or corroded end caps. Replace if any evidence of damage.

Step 8: To test heater set ohmmeter to R x 1 scale. Place probes on terminals at each end cap. Read resistance. Meter should sweep partially upscale. If ohmmeter does not move, replace the heater (s).

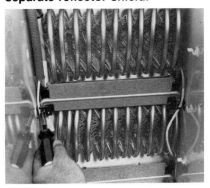

Step 9: Replace multiple heaters as a set. When one heater in a series has failed, replacement of only one heater will cause early failure of other heaters.

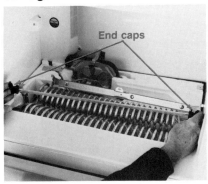

Step 10: Handle heater by end caps only, do not touch glass. Salt deposits from hands could cause premature failure. If you do accidently touch glass, wipe with damp paper towel. Do not use cloth.

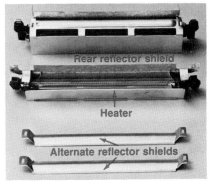

Step 11: On models where more than one heater is used, use kit without modification if old heater has rear reflector shield. If old heater does not have rear reflector, modify by replacing original shield with alternate shield in kit.

Step 12: To replace heater(s), position end caps into saddle bracket. Replace reflector shield(s). Reconnect push-on connectors. Arrange wires to prevent burning. Reassemble appliance and reconnect power supply.

Procedure 22
Inspecting and replacing relay

The relay on a refrigerator or freezer starts the compressor motor. The relay momentarily energizes the start winding to start the rotation of the compressor motor. On most models, a current-sensing type relay is used that consists of an armature, solenoid coil, and set of contacts.

When line voltage is applied to the line terminal of the relay and the common terminal of the compressor motor, a heavy current surges through the run winding and relay coil. This creates a strong magnetic field which closes the contacts and energizes the start winding. This in turn starts the rotation of the compressor motor. As the motor accelerates to nearly full speed, the run winding current diminishes and the magnetic field reduces, thus opening the contacts. The compressor motor then continues to operate on the run winding only.

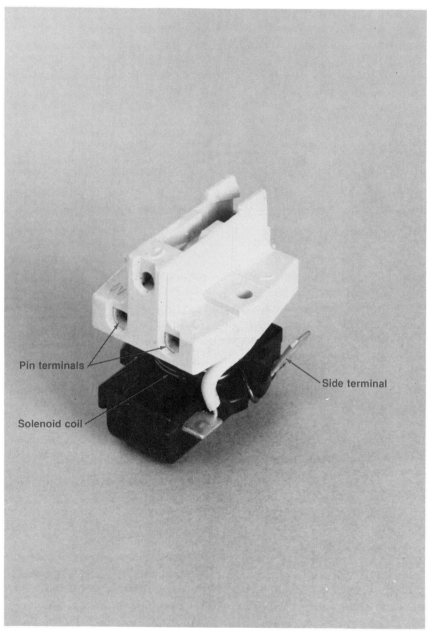

Relay

Relay (continued)

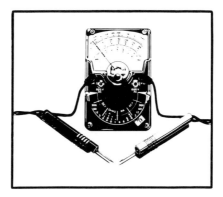

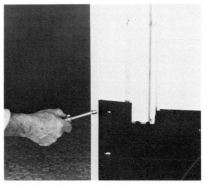

Step 1: UNPLUG the refrigerator or freezer from the wall receptacle. Watch for sharp edges inside machine compartment.

Step 2: This procedure requires the use of an ohmmeter. For instructions, please refer to Tools and Testing Equipment page 98.

Step 3: Remove lower rear access panel. If you are unfamiliar with this process, please refer to Procedure #3: Removing Access Panels.

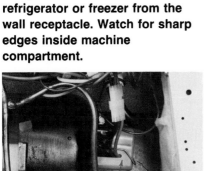

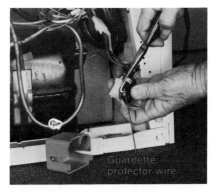

Step 4: Lift up terminal cover retainer clip. Remove terminal cover by pulling away from compressor case. Cover will house Guardette® protector and relay.

Step 5: Pull relay straight off of compressor. Avoid moving relay side to side or up and down. This can damage relay and compressor terminals.

Step 6: On some models, remove Guardette® protector wire attached to side of relay. Grip terminal with pliers and pull straight off to remove. Avoid damaging terminals with pliers.

Step 7: Release pin terminal from top of relay. Hold terminal firmly. Lift up and pull out of relay cavity.

Step 8: Visually inspect relay for signs of corrosion or overheated (discolored) terminals. If corroded or discolored, replace relay. Check pin terminal on wire release. If corroded, terminal and wire should be replaced.

Step 9: Check relay coil for continuity. Set ohmmeter at R x 1. Place probes at "L" (side) and "M" terminals. Needle should sweep upscale to zero.

Relay (continued)

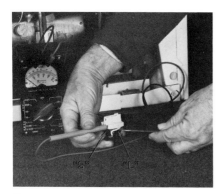

Step 10: To check relay contacts, set ohmmeter at R x 1 scale. Place one probe on "L" (side) terminal, and the other on "S" terminal. Ohmmeter needle should not move.

Step 11: Turn relay upside down (opposite of normal mounting position). Place one probe on "L" and other probe on "S" terminal. Ohmmeter needle should sweep upscale to zero. If relay fails any test, replace.

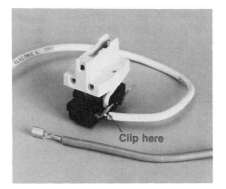

Step 12: Some replacement relays have an auxillary wire attached which connects to a 3-terminal condenser fan motor. If your model has a two-terminal condenser fan motor, clip this wire off close to connection point on relay and discard.

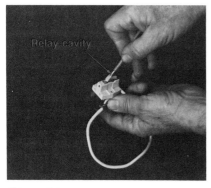

Step 13: To reinstall wires on relay, the flat side of pin terminal should be at top. Insert pin terminal back into relay cavity. Splice auxilliary wire to harness if your model has 3-terminal condenser fan.

Step 14: To install new relay, push relay fully on compressor terminals to assure good connection.

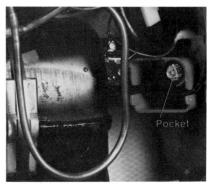

Step 15: Position Guardette® protector in terminal cover for installation. A "pocket" is provided in terminal cover to secure protector position. Arrange wires through slots in terminal cover.

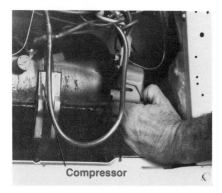

Step 16: Install the terminal cover with Guardette® protector firmly positioned against compressor. Press retainer clip down over cover and latch in place.

Step 17: Reassemble refrigerator or freezer and reconnect power supply.

Notes

Procedure 23
Inspecting and replacing Guardette® protector

Skill Level Rating: | Easy | Average | Difficult | **Very Difficult** |

The Guardette® motor protector is a safety feature on your refrigerator or freezer. Should the compressor motor overheat or fail to start, the Guardette® protector interrupts power to the compressor motor. The Guardette® protector is mounted in direct contact with the compressor case.

Inside the protector is a bimetal element which is sensitive to heat and current. Should either heat or current reach an unsafe level, the Guardette® protector contacts snap open and interrupt current flow. Upon cooling, the bimetal element flexes, closing the contacts. The compressor motor will continue to cycle on and off so long as the original reason for tripping persists. What may seem like "nuisance tripping" is usually dependable Guardette® protector operation, protecting the compressor motor from outside causes, such as low voltage, temporary power outage, etc.

CAUTION: A Guardette® protector should NEVER be by-passed in the circuit. Never replace with Guardette® protector of a different rating.

Guardette® protector

Step 1: UNPLUG the refrigerator or freezer from the wall receptacle. Watch for sharp edges inside machine compartment.

Step 2: This procedure requires the use of an ohmmeter. For instructions, please refer to Tools and Testing Equipment, page 98.

Step 3: Remove lower rear access panel. If you are unfamiliar with this process, please refer to Procedure #3: Removing Access Panels.

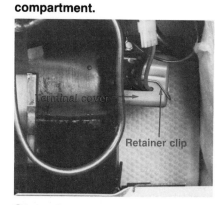

Step 4: Lift up terminal cover retainer clip. Remove terminal cover by pulling away from compressor case. Cover houses relay and Guardette® protector. On some models, protector may be held in place by a retainer strap.

Step 5: Pull relay straight off compressor. Avoid moving relay side to side or up and down. This can damage relay and compressor terminals.

Step 6: On some models, remove Guardette® protector wires attached to side of relay. Grip terminal with pliers and pull straight off to remove. Avoid damaging terminals with pliers.

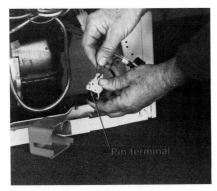

Step 7: On models where Guardette® protector wire attaches to relay top terminal, release wire and terminal by lifting wire up and pulling out of relay cavity.

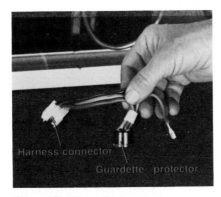

Step 8: Visually inspect Guardette® protector for signs of corrosion, discoloration, or broken wires. If there is visible damage, replace Guardette® protector. Do not attempt to solder wires to Guardette® protector terminals.

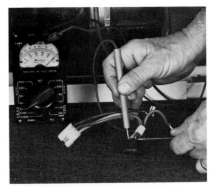

Step 9: Check protector for continuity. Set ohmmeter to R x 1. Place one probe on each protector terminal. Ohmmeter needle should sweep to zero. If not, replace protector.

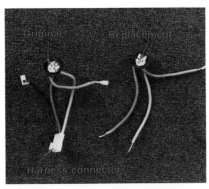

Step 10: Carefully compare wires on replacement protector with inoperative protector before making connections. Replacement Guardette® protectors usually have 3 wires. If original Guardette® protector has only 2 wires, snip off extra wire.

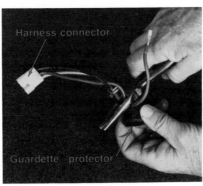

Step 11: Cut wires to be spliced from inoperative protector close to welded terminals. This will allow splices to be located outside of terminal cover.

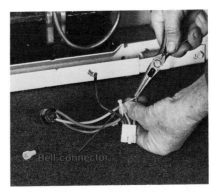

Step 12: The protector wires must be spliced to wiring harness. Use closed end "bell" connectors to splice wire. Reattach Guardette® protector wire to relay.

Step 13: Push relay on compressor terminals. Position Guardette® protector in "pocket" of terminal cover and arrange wires through slots in cover.

Step 14: Install terminal cover with Guardette® protector in direct contact with compressor. Press retainer clip down and latch in place.

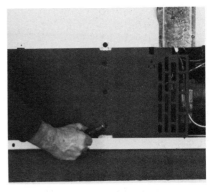

Step 15: Reassemble refrigerator or freezer and reconnect power supply.

Procedure 24
Testing compressor motor

The compressor motor is directly mounted to the compressor and is located inside a sealed steel case. The compressor motor has two windings--a start winding and a run winding. These windings are connected internally to glass-sealed terminals on the compressor case. On most compressors, the terminals are clustered in a triangular pattern, consisting of a start, common, and run terminal.

Note: The compressor is part of the sealed refrigeration system that should be repaired only by a qualified service technician. Tests can be made, however, on the compressor to determine whether the compressor motor has failed.

Compressor

Step 1: UNPLUG the refrigerator or freezer from the wall receptacle. Watch for sharp edges inside machine compartment.

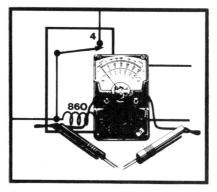

Step 2: This procedure requires the use of an ohmmeter and the ability to read a circuit diagram. For instructions, please refer to Tools and Testing Equipment, pages 98-100.

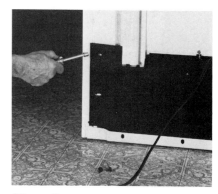

Step 3: Remove the lower rear access panel. If you are unfamiliar with this process, please refer to Procedure #3: Removing Access Panels.

Step 4: Noise from machine compartment may be due to compressor loose in mounts. Test for solidity with hand. Tighten screws on retaining brackets at rear and front of appliance.

Step 5: Other vibration noise may be caused by insulation or padding slipping or a misplaced drain pan. Make a visual check and reposition padding, if necessary.

Step 6: To test compressor motor, lift up terminal retainer clip. Remove terminal cover by pulling away from compressor case. Cover houses relay and Guardette® protector.

Compressor motor (continued)

Step 7: Pull relay off of compressor. Avoid moving relay side-to-side or up-and-down. Such movement can damage relay and compressor terminals.

Step 8: After removing relay, you can locate three compressor terminals clustered in a triangle.

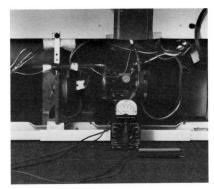

Step 9: To test these terminals, a series of three separate readings must be compared with the circuit diagram from your appliance. For the first series of tests, set ohmmeter to R x 1 scale.

Step 10: Test 1. Place one probe on start winding; other probe on run winding. Compare reading with sum total of the two windings shown on the circuit diagram. Reading may be substantially higher if compressor is hot.

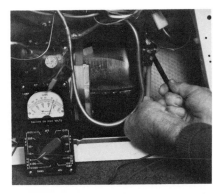

Step 11: Test 2. Place one probe on start winding and other probe on the common terminal. Compare this reading with the circuit diagram.

Step 12: Test 3. Place one probe on the run winding and other probe on the common terminal. Compare with circuit diagram data. If any of three tests show no reading or lower reading than circuit diagram, compressor has failed.

Step 13: The second series of tests should be made by setting ohmmeter to highest range, R x 1000 or higher. Check each terminal individually by placing one probe on terminal and other probe to bare metal on compressor case.

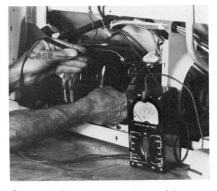

Step 14: When testing with ohmmeter, be sure to touch probe to metal on compressor case, not painted surface. (Scratch paint away, if necessary). Ohmmeter needle should not move. If ohmmeter test indicates continuity, compressor has failed. Call qualified service technician.

Step 15: If the compressor does not operate and no defect is found with the compressor after testing with ohmmeter, compressor may or may not be at fault. Further (conclusive) testing must be done by a qualified service technician.

Procedure 25
Inspecting and replacing water valve

Skill Level Rating: | Easy | Average | Difficult | **Very Difficult**

A water valve is used on a refrigerator with an icemaker or a chilled water dispenser. The water valve is vital to the automatic operation of the icemaker or dispenser. A switch in the icemaker or dispenser closes the circuit to the valve, allowing the valve to open as water is needed. Should the valve become clogged with mineral deposits or sediment, the water supply can be totally cut off. In the case of a defective valve, water could continue to flow.

A dual function valve is used on models with a chilled water dispenser. Both single function and dual function valves require the same basic testing and replacement steps.

Note: Water valves may require additional testing that must be performed by a qualified service technician.

Single function water valve

Step 1: UNPLUG the refrigerator from the wall receptacle. Watch for sharp edges in machine compartment.

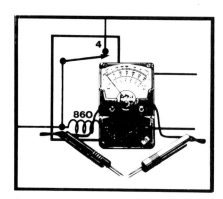

Step 2: This procedure requires the use of an ohmmeter and the ability to read a circuit diagram. For instructions, please refer to Tools and Testing Equipment, pages 98-100.

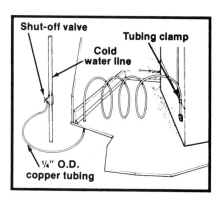

Step 3: Shut off water supply at shut-off valve. The shut-off valve is part of your household plumbing. Check household valve for proper installation.

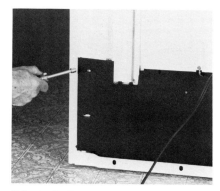

Step 4: This procedure requires the removal of the access cover on your refrigerator. If you are unfamiliar with this process, please refer to Procedure #3: Removing Access Panels.

Step 5: Mineral deposits inside valve could restrict water supply. Check and clean valve screen. Disconnect tubing at flare nut, place container under tubing, and turn water supply on. If water does not flow, problem is with household plumbing.

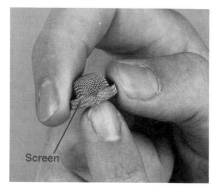

Step 6: Remove valve screen by prying from valve taking care not to damage screen. Clean screen with running water. Refit into valve. **NOTE:** It may be necessary to reform screen slightly after removal.

Water valve (continued)

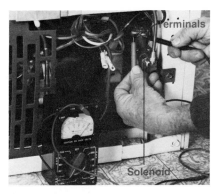

Step 7: To test valve, set ohmmeter to R × 100. Remove push-on connectors. Place probes on water valve solenoid terminals. Meter should sweep partially upscale. If meter needle does not move, replace valve.

Step 8: When testing dual function valve, note location of connections for reinstallation reference. Dual function valve connections are color-coded: White/orange lead connects to icemaker; blue/orange lead connects to dispenser.

Step 9: To test dual function valve, test one solenoid at a time following instructions for single valve in Step 6. If either solenoid is open, replace defective solenoid. Solenoids can be replaced separately without replacing complete valve.

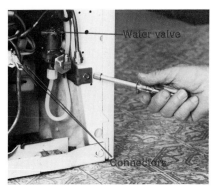

Step 10: To replace valve, disconnect push-on connectors and fittings from tubing on water valve. Be careful not to damage fittings or tubing. Remove valve from machine compartment by removing screw from bracket.

Step 11: To install new water valve, reconnect push-on connectors and plastic tubing to valve outlet. Attach new valve to cabinet with screw in existing hole. Reconnect water supply tubing and tighten firmly.

Step 12: On dual function valve, push-on connectors must be reconnected to proper solenoid to avoid reversing functions.

Step 13: Outlet water tubing on dual valve is a different size and will not interchange. Larger outlet serves dispenser; smaller tubing serves icemaker.

Step 14: Turn water on and check for leaks. If a leak exists, tighten flare nut no more than half a turn. Take care not to damage fitting.

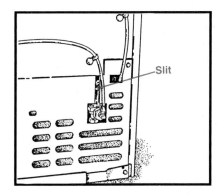

Step 15: Replace back access cover. Cover may require slitting to facilitate installation over water supply tubing. Plastic water line should be directed out of compartmant and up back of refrigerator. Reconnect power supply.

Procedure 26
Inspecting and replacing water filter

Skill Level Rating: | Easy | Average | **Difficult** | Very Difficult |

All water contains some dissolved mineral, primarily calcium carbonate. When water contains a considerable amount of minerals, it is often referred to as "hard" water. Water can have an odor, an off color, or contain sediment. Many of the impurities in water can be removed by installing a water filter on the refrigerator water supply line. The water filter is available in kit form. The water is filtered through a charcoal filter within a replaceable cartridge. Change filter cartridge every 12 months or more frequently if heavy mineral or other conditions exist. Smaller than normal ice cubes may indicate filter needs replacing. Record installation date for future reference.

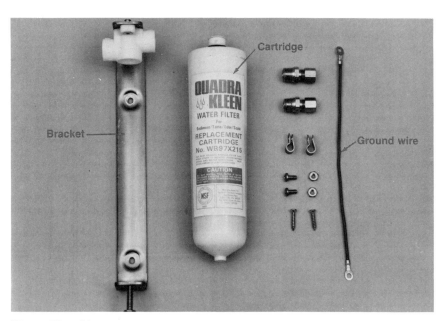

Water filter kit

Step 1: UNPLUG the refrigerator or freezer from the wall receptacle. Watch for sharp edges.

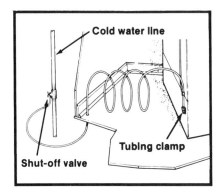

Step 2: Shut off the water supply valve. Determine location for installing water filter. For best results install filter as near as possible to refrigerator water connection. Other locations can be under sink, in cabinet, or in basement.

Step 3: The water filter can be installed at any convenient point along the length of the 1/4" (outside diameter) copper supply line. Water filter must have 2" clearance at base of mounting bracket for cartridge replacement.

Water filter (continued)

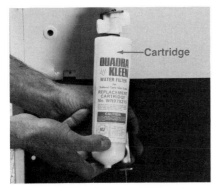

Step 4: To install mounting bracket, remove cartridge. Unscrew wing screw until it is flush with bracket. Pull filter cartridge straight down and forward. Reinstall cartridge after bracket is screwed in place.

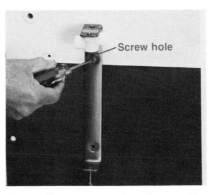

Step 5: To mount bracket on the back of refrigerator, use existing screw hole and one of the supplied screws. Clamps on tubing will give additional support. A tubing clamp is also furnished in filter kit.

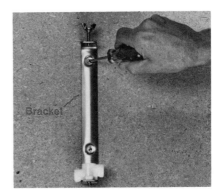

Step 6: Water filter can be mounted in other locations such as in a cabinet, under sink. Place bracket in position. Mark location of both screw holes. Drill or punch holes slightly smaller than screws furnished. Install screws to hold bracket firmly.

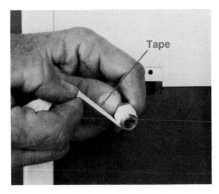

Step 7: Apply supplied tape to threads on brass fittings. Start one or two threads back from end and wrap tape tightly in same direction as threads. Overlap tape and slightly stretch it. Press tape into threads with fingers.

Step 8: Screw tape wrapped brass fittings into filter head. Hand tighten, then tighten the fittings with a wrench, not more than two full turns. Do not over tighten.

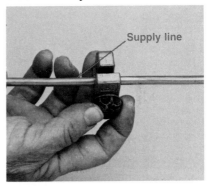

Step 9: Before cutting supply line, make sure sufficient tubing remains to allow refrigerator to be moved away from wall. Cut tubing with tubing cutter.

Step 10: Slide the furnished compression nut and compression ring over each end of the copper tubing.

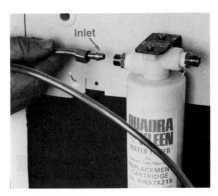

Step 11: Insert supply line (from water supply valve) into the fitting in the inlet of filter head. Tighten compression nut using a wrench, while holding filter inlet fitting with second wrench. (Arrows on filter head indicate water flow).

Step 12: Insert the supply line carrying water to refrigerator into the outlet of filter head. Use the same method as in Step 11.

Water filter (continued)

Step 13: Disconnect the tubing clamp and flare nut at the refrigerator connection. Place a container below the end of connection and turn on water to flush filter. Allow about one pint of water to flow through filter.

Step 14: Reconnect the tubing at the refrigerator connection. Turn water supply on and check for leaks at both filter and refrigerator connections. It may not be necessary to remove access cover for this procedure.

Step 15: If a leak exists between the brass fitting and plastic filter head, tighten no more than an additional half turn. Check tape and rewrap if necessary.

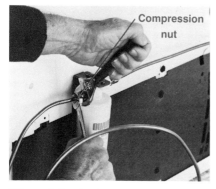

Step 16: If a leak exists at the compression nut, use a wrench to tighten nut while holding the fitting in the filter head. To prevent from turning entire fitting, use two wrenches.

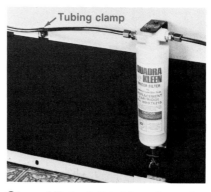

Step 17: Install tubing clamp in existing hole in back of the refrigerator. Position one clamp on the tubing at the filter inlet using the furnished clamp and screw in filter kit.

Step 18: For installation of filter, other than at back of refrigerator, position clamps on tubing one inch back from the compression nuts.

Step 19: Install ground wire to tubing clamps using screws and nuts. To insure good ground continuity, make sure clamps are tight. Reconnect power supply.

Notes

Procedure 27
Inspecting and repairing water dispenser

Skill Level Rating: | Easy | Average | Difficult | **Very Difficult**

Ice and water dispensers are convenience features on some GE/Hotpoint refrigerators. Some models are equipped to dispense ice cubes, crushed ice, and chilled water. Other models are equipped to dispense ice cubes and chilled water, ice cubes and crushed ice, ice cubes only, or chilled water only. These convenience features are served through an exterior dispensing recess.

Although variations exist in the external appearance of the dispenser recess on the freezer door, the basic dispenser components are essentially the same for all models. Major components are a water valve, located at the rear of the refrigerator; a water reservoir, located in the fresh food compartment; and a recess assembly, mounted on the freezer door.

Water and ice dispenser

Water dispenser (continued)

Step 1: Some simple diagnostic tests may be performed before disconnecting refrigerator from power supply. Practice safe work habits.

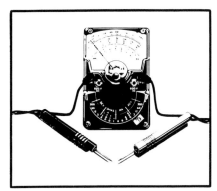

Step 2: This procedure requires the use of an ohmmeter. For instructions, please refer to Tools and Testing Equipment, page 98.

Step 3: There are several tests that can be performed to pinpoint water dispenser problems. You may wish to perform these tests prior to attempting repairs.

Step 4: No water valve "buzz" and no water delivery may be the result of a water valve problem. On models so equipped, ice delivery but no water also may indicate water valve problems. Refer to Procedure #25: Inspecting and Replacing Water Valve.

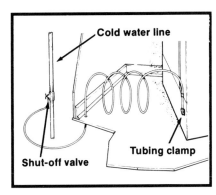

Step 5: If no ice or water is delivered, problem may be with household water supply. Check for obstructions. Check tubing at rear of refrigerator.

Step 6: Warm water delivery may be normal. Water dispensed from dispenser feature is not "ice" water, but is chilled to a temperature slightly warmer than fresh food compartment. Discard first glass, and refill.

Step 7: If a normal water valve "buzz" is heard, but no water is delivered check for frozen water reservoir, leakage, or frozen tubing.

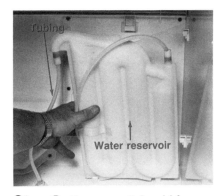

Step 8: Remove all food bins and lower shelving from fresh food compartment. Make a visual inspection of water reservoir, tubing, and refrigerator floor.

Step 9: If water reservoir is frozen, allow tubing and reservoir to thaw. Check for correct temperature. If you are unfamiliar with this process, refer to Procedure #5: Temperature Testing.

Water dispenser (continued)

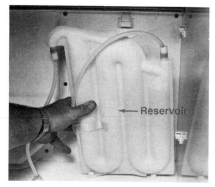

Step 10: Water standing on fresh food compartment floor can indicate a leak from tubing, fitting, or reservoir. Hold reservoir up while depressing water dispenser to locate source of leak.

Step 11: UNPLUG your refrigerator from wall receptacle before proceeding to other steps or attempting other repairs. Watch for sharp edges.

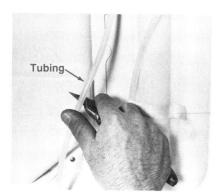

Step 12: If water reservoir or tubing has visible leak, cut tubing with sharp knife. If replacing reservoir, cut tubing 6″ from water reservoir connection. Note that some water collected in tubing may spill at this time.

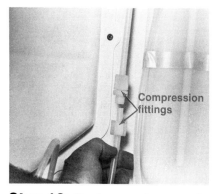

Step 13: Replacement reservoir has bonded tubing and requires compression fittings to connect existing tubing with water reservoir. Make sure tubing is cut straight and is free of burrs.

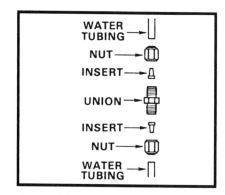

Step 14: Place nut over tubing and the insert into the open end of tubing. Position tubing fully into fitting and hand tighten nut. Use a wrench to tighten <u>slightly</u> to assure a water-tight connection.

Step 15: After installing reservoir, reconnect power supply and depress water cradle to check for leaks, allowing enough time for air to be forced from tubing and reservoir.

Step 16: Purge water from reservoir to eliminate any plastic taste from new reservoir. Water filter installation may be necessary to remove other tastes. See Procedure #26: Installing Water Filter.

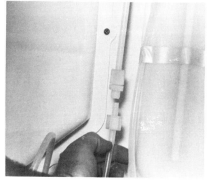

Step 17: On models with tubing bonded to reservoir, tubing can be replaced by cutting and splicing if leak is within fresh food compartment. An obvious (water on floor) leak in the internal routing of tubing requires replacement by a qualified service technician.

Step 18: If water valve and water supply are functioning properly, and no leak is apparent in reservoir, check the dispenser switch.

Water dispenser (continued)

Step 19: Inspect rear of dispenser. Some dispenser covers may be held in place by screws; others are held in place by hooks and tabs.

Step 20: To remove cover without screws, first press upward on inner door panel, near center, just above cover, while pulling outward on top of cover with fingertips. Use care not to damage cover or clips.

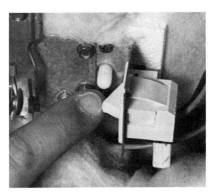

Step 21: Carefully move insulation to locate switch assembly for water.

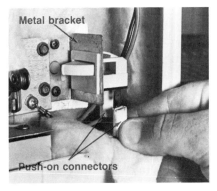

Step 22: Remove push-on connectors, making note of position for reinstallation when reassembling the dispenser.

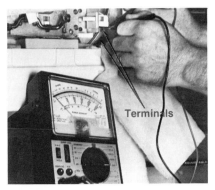

Step 23: To test switch, set ohmmeter to R × 1 setting. Place test probes on switch terminals. Needle should not move. Depress water cradle on dispenser front. Needle should sweep to zero. If either test fails, replace switch.

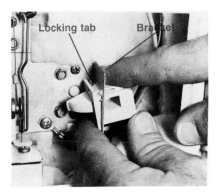

Step 24: To remove old switch, press down top locking tab and remove switch from metal bracket. Insert new switch and push into bracket until tab "snaps" in place. Replace push-on connectors.

Step 25: Reassemble refrigerator and reconnect power supply.

Procedure 28
Inspecting and replacing icemaker

Skill Level Rating: | Easy | Average | **Difficult** | Very Difficult

An icemaker replaces the ice you use automatically and keeps the ice bin filled with a ready supply of cubes. The convenience of "automatic ice" is accomplished by a five-phase icemaking cycle, consisting of 1) freeziing, 2) releasing, 3) ejecting, 4) sweeping, and 5) filling with water.

The mold fills with water, and freezing takes place. When cubes are frozen, the operating thermostat closes, energizing the motor and mold heater. The motor tries to turn, but is stalled by the frozen ice. The motor remains in this stalled condition for two to four minutes or until the heater has melted the ice free from the mold. When the ice is melted free, the motor turns to operate 1) the ejector lever that pushes the cubes upward and out of the mold, and 2) the feeler arm that sweeps the cubes into the ice bin.

The icemaker mechanism returns to its original position, energizing the water fill switch to let water refill the mold. When the maximum ice level is reached, the feeler arm comes to rest on the ice, stopping further cycles until ice is removed from the bin.

Some models with exterior dispenser service use a photo-sensing icemaker that does not have a feeler arm. A high intensity light source controls the icemaker cycles. A beam passes across the top of the ice bin to strike a photo switch. When the beam is broken by a full ice bin, the cycle stops.

Note: Each icemaker is identified with a catalog number. An identification plate is attached to the icemaker with this number. When replacing your icemaker, refer to this number for correct replacement.

CAUTION: Do not place fingers or hands on the automatic icemaking mechanism when the refrigerator is plugged in.

CAUTION: Under certain rare circumstances, ice cubes may be discolored, usually appearing with a bluish-green hue. Continued consumption of such discolored ice cubes may be hazardous to your health. If such discoloration is observed, contact your local GE/ Hotpoint service representative.

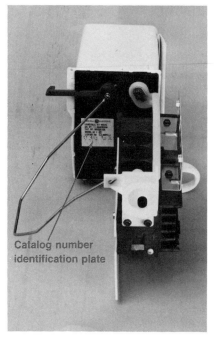

Catalog number identification plate

Icemaker

Icemaker (continued)

Step 1: UNPLUG the refrigerator from the wall receptacle. Watch for sharp edges.

Step 2: Make a visual inspection of the icemaker. A check for obvious problems may offer a simple solution. Make sure the shut-off control is in "ON" position. Check for food packages obstructing feeler arm movement.

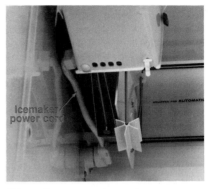

Step 3: Check icemaker power cord. An improper or loose connection could be the cause of intermittent operation or no operation.

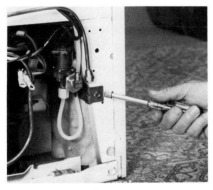

Step 4: Insufficient water supply can cause a low fill at the icemaker. Check for a water leak. Water on floor or water leaking from fittings may cause improper fill. Also check water valve. Refer to Procedure #25: Inspecting and Replacing Water Valve.

Step 5: For optimum performance, freezer temperature should be between 0 and 8°F. Either low or high temperatures can cause icemaker problems. Refer to Procedure #5: Temperature Testing.

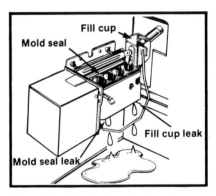

Step 6: Check for obvious leaks in bin or on freezer floor. Water dripping from or forming icicles on the icemaker indicate leak in mold seal or fill cup seal. Refer to Procedure #29: Inspecting and Replacing Icemaker Seal Assemblies.

Step 7: Check ice cubes. Small size, liquid center, or cubes outside bin in freezer compartment indicate possible icemaker malfunction. If you have one of these problems, refer to the Technical Assistance section on page 93.

Step 8: If icemaker removal is necessary for service or unit replacement, loosen two screws at top of icemaker that thread into freezer side wall.

Step 9: After loosening screws, lift icemaker up and off screw supports. Some models may have an additional support bracket at top of freezer.

Icemaker (continued)

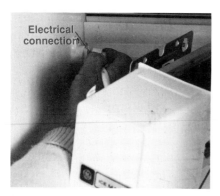

Step 10: Unplug icemaker power cord from electrical connection. Note location of water fill tube extension for correct replacement of icemaker.

Step 11: When replacing an icemaker, it is sometimes necessary to transfer some components to the new replacement unit.

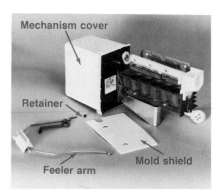

Step 12: Make note of original component location for future installation reference.

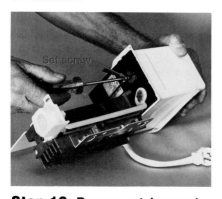

Step 13: Remove retainer and set screw. Remove feeler arm and shut-off control lever. Remove mold shield by removing two screws.

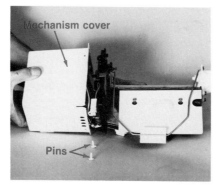

Step 14: Most icemakers have decorative trims and/or gaskets attached to the mechanism cover. To avoid transferring these, transfer the entire cover. Remove two pins. Slide original cover onto new icemaker. Reinsert pins.

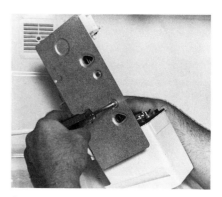

Step 15: Transfer liner shield and tighten both screws securely. Liner shield acts as heat sink to protect plastic freezer liner from heat damage from icemaker.

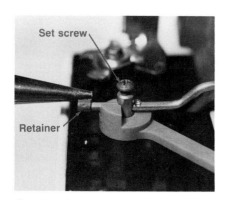

Step 16: To reinstall feeler arm, place shut-off control in "ON" position and insert feeler arm. Tighten set screw and install new retainer. Set icemaker to "OFF" position.

Step 17: To install icemaker, rest icemaker on shelf or freezer floor. Plug icemaker power cord into electrical connection with prongs matched to corresponding holes. Make sure plug is firmly seated in socket.

Step 18: Lift icemaker and position rear opening to fill tube. Hang icemaker on two screws on freezer wall. Tighten screws securely.

Icemaker (continued)

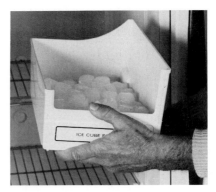

Step 19: Reconnect refrigerator power cord. Set shut-off control to "ON" position.

Step 20: Icemaking cycle will not begin until the icemaker reaches operating temperatures and then icemaking will begin automatically.

Step 21: Record date of replacement for future reference. When icemaker is first connected or reconnected after extended periods of non-use, discard first few batches of ice.

Inspecting and replacing icemaker seal assemblies

Skill Level Rating:	Easy	Average	Difficult	**Very Difficult**

As with any water-carrying appliance, the icemaker could be subject to occasional leaks. The most common leak occurs where the ejector rod passes through the icemaker mold (bottom center of icemaker). The replacement of the mold seal assembly requires partial disassembly of the icemaker and should only be attempted by experienced do-it-yourselfers. To replace the mold seal assembly, you will need a mold seal kit and two special installation tools. To find the nearest sales location for these repair items, call the GE Answer Center® consumer information service toll free at 800-626-2000.

Another source of water leakage is at the back of the icemaker where the fill bup attaches to the mold. This is a relatively easy repair requiring a **non-toxic** sealant and minor disassembly.

CAUTION: Some types of sealants contain materials that could be hazardous to your health. Be sure to use a **non-toxic** sealant such as GE product 361, Silicone Household Glue & Seal, catalog number WX6X101, when resealing the fill cup.

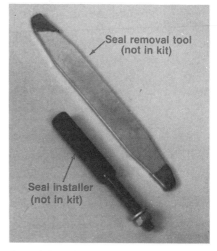

Special tools for mold seal replacement

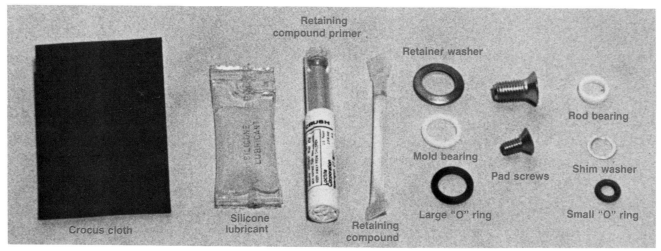

Mold seal kit

Step 1: UNPLUG the refrigerator from the wall receptacle. Watch for sharp edges.

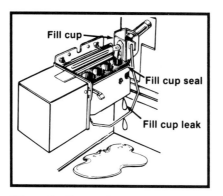

Step 2: Determine area of leak. If leak is at rear of icemaker, look for fused or lumped cubes in rear of ice bin. Mineral deposits may also be present at rear of icemaker, indicating a fill cup problem. If this is not your problem, go to Step 7.

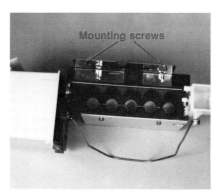

Step 3: Remove icemaker from mounting brackets and unplug icemaker power cord from electrical connection. If you are unfamiliar with this process, refer to Procedure #28: Inspecting and Replacing Icemaker.

Icemaker seal assemblies (continued)

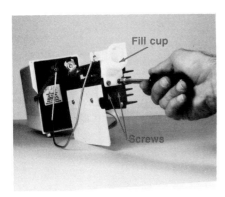

Step 4: Set icemaker on table and allow to warm slightly. Remove screws from fill cup. Carefully brush away any loose mineral deposits. Make sure icemaker is clean and totally dry.

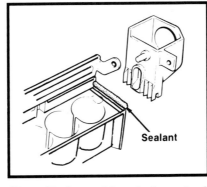

Step 5: Spread bead of non-toxic sealant (such as GE product 361, Silicone Household Glue & Seal, catalog no. WX6X101) along rear edge of mold. Reinstall fill cup, making sure to spread sealant evenly. **CAUTION:** Make sure sealant is non-toxic.

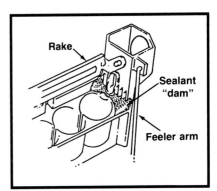

Step 6: With feeler arm in place, apply additional sealant to form a "dam" as shown. Build up and shape corners, making sure sealant does not interfere with rake movement or cube ejection. Allow sealant to dry several hours. Go to Step 30.

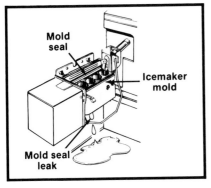

Step 7: If water is leaking or forming icicles at center of icemaker mold, you may have to replace the mold seal. This is a difficult procedure and should only be attempted by experienced do-it-yourselfers.

Step 8: Remove icemaker from mounting brackets and unplug icemaker power cord from electrical connection. If you are unfamiliar with this process, refer to Procedure #28: Inspecting and Replacing Icemaker.

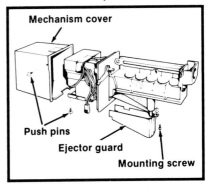

Step 9: Pry two plastic push pins loose from bottom and side of mechanism cover with flat-blade screwdriver and lift off cover. Unfasten ejector guard by removing mounting screw with ¼" nutdriver.

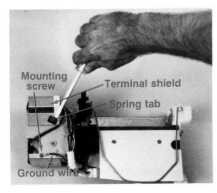

Step 10: Unscrew terminal shield mounting screw with ¼" nutdriver. Lift off ground wire. Gently pry loose spring tab with thin flat-blade screwdriver and lift off shield.

Step 11: Grip center of spring firmly with pliers. Pry end near top of icemaker out with flat-blade screwdriver. **CAUTION:** Spring is under tension and may release suddenly.

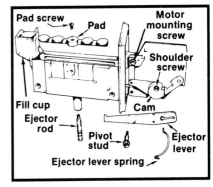

Step 12: Remove pivot stud by unscrewing motor mounting screw with 5/16" nutdriver. Loosen screw four turns. To remove ejector lever, slide it toward motor so keyhole slot clears cam shoulder screw.

Icemaker seal assemblies (continued)

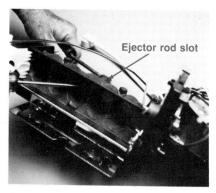

Step 13: Insert a blade screwdriver in slot of ejector rod. Hold pad screw with Phillips screwdriver while turning ejector rod with blade screwdriver. Remove ejector rod, pad screw, and pad.

Step 14: Compare pad screw to pad screws provided in mold seal kit. Select correct replacement screw and apply retaining compound primer. Set primed screw aside to dry. Discard old screw.

Step 15: Remove the seal retainer washer with the special seal removal tool. Remove bearing and "O" ring. Discard these parts, as they will be replaced from mold seal kit and not reused.

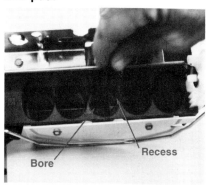

Step 16: Clean recess and inside bore with clean soft cloth. Take care to remove all particles of old seal to allow for proper seating of new seal.

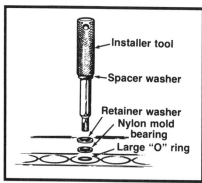

Step 17: Remove nut and washer from seal installer tool, leaving black spacer washer on tool. Clean tool shaft. Place retainer washer on shaft with "crowned" side against spacer washer.

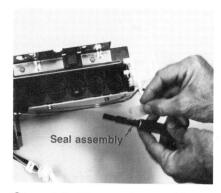

Step 18: Place nylon mold bearing followed by large "O" ring next to retainer washer. Apply a generous amount of silicone lubricant to seal assembly on shaft of tool.

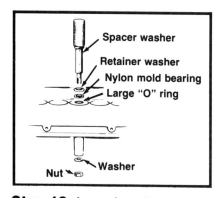

Step 19: Insert installer tool into mold from the top. Place washer and nut on tool and tighten to a hard pull using ½" open-end wrench.

Step 20: Remove the tool and inspect for proper seating. The "crowned" side of the retainer should be flattened. Make sure spacer washer does not remain in mold when tool is removed.

Step 21: Polish the ejector rod with the crocus cloth and check for irregularities. Replace if pitted.

Icemaker seal assemblies (continued)

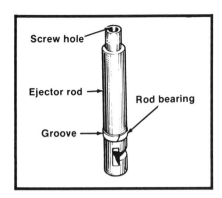

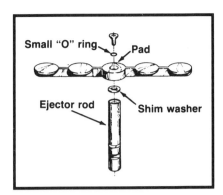

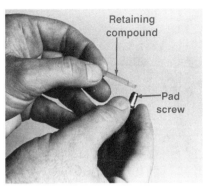

Step 22: Install the new rod bearing into groove on ejector rod. Coat rod and bearing with silicone lubricant. Do not allow lubricant to leak into screw hole. With shim washer in position on upper end of ejector rod, reinstall rod into mold from bottom, aligning pad to ejector rod.

Step 23: On icemaker pads with a deep recess in pad, use the small "O" ring on the pad screw up against the head. On other icemakers, apply non-toxic sealant to beveled surface of pad. After screw is driven, wipe off any excess sealant.

Step 24: Coat the new pad screw (primed earlier) with retaining compound. Insert screw through pad and into ejector rod. Hold pad in position in the bottom of the mold and align ejector rod slot with ejector lever, while firmly tightening the pad screw.

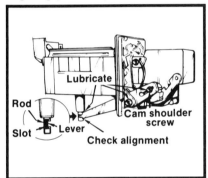

Step 25: Lubricate the ejector lever with silicone lubricant at tip, hole, and slot. Reinstall ejector lever, engaging slot in the lever with the cam shoulder screw and the tip of the lever in the slot in the ejector rod.

Step 26: Check alignment of ejector lever with ejector rod slot, while holding pad in position in bottom of mold. If binding condition exists between ejector lever and ejector rod slot, improper seating will result.

Step 27: Reinstall the pivot stud making sure white spacer washers (if used) are in position between the mold and motor brackets. Firmly tighten the pivot stud and the upper motor mounting screw.

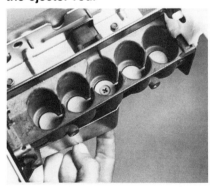

Step 28: Reinstall ejector lever spring (refer back to steps 11 and 12). Check for proper seating of the pad in the bottom of the mold by pushing up on the ejector rod and allowing the ejector lever spring to return the pad.

Step 29: Replace terminal shield and mechanism cover. Reattach ground wire and spring tab. Make sure power cord and test receptacle grommets are properly fitted into cover slots. Replace ejector guard.

Step 30: Reinstall icemaker as described in Procedure #28. Make sure liner shield (heat sink) and icemaker power cord are in place. Check for correct position of fill tube. Turn shut-off control to "ON". Discard first batches of ice.

Technical assistance/Service record

This page is provided as a convenient reference for important refrigerator and freezer repair information. There are spaces for you to record your refrigerator and freezer model number, parts needed, repair notes (such as where wire leads reattach), and when repairs were made. There are also spaces for you to write down the phone numbers of your nearest GE/Hotpoint parts dealer and Factory Service Center.

Model number: (Refrigerator) _____ (Freezer) _____

Icemaker catalog number: _____

Parts or components needed:

_____

_____

Repair notes:

_____

_____

Service record:

_____

_____

Water shut-off valve location: _____

Fuse or circuit breaker location: _____

Size fuse required: _____

Phone number of GE/Hotpoint Factory Service Center: _____

Preventive maintenance

At GE, we're committed to your satisfaction. The basic do's and don'ts included in this section are our way of helping you obtain the best results from your GE/Hotpoint refrigerator or freezer. The few minutes you invest in caring for your refrigerator or freezer properly can save you a great deal of time and trouble.

This section outlines basic precautions and simple maintenance routines that will help prevent the small problems that can lead to big repair jobs. Take a little time to read this part of the manual and follow the advice given.

Installation tips
- When using your appliance always exercise basic safety precautions.
- Use your refrigerator or freezer only for its intended purpose.
- When moving your appliance, move it **straight** out to prevent damage to floor coverings.
- Be careful not to roll over the power cord when moving your refrigerator.
- Never unplug your appliance by pulling on the power cord.
- Be sure to install your refrigerator or freezer on a floor strong enough to fully support the appliance when it is fully loaded.
- Do not install your refrigerator or freezer where temperatures will fall below 60 degrees.

Refrigerator or freezer exterior maintenance
- Do not use scouring powder or any abrasive cleaner on the exterior surface of your refrigerator or freezer.
- Apply a coat of appliance polish wax to your refrigerator or freezer at least twice a year to keep a new looking appearance.
- If the exterior of your refrigerator or freezer should become soiled, wipe it off with a **clean** cloth lightly dampened with appliance polish wax or mild household detergent. Use a **clean**, soft cloth to dry and polish the cleaned surface.
- If your appliance has a condenser mounted on the back, be sure to keep it free of all obstructions. Items placed on top of the appliance can easily slip off and down into the condenser.
- An onyx (black glass) front on refrigerators can be cleaned with mild soap and water.

Refrigerator and freezer maintenance
- Clean the inside of your appliance at least once a year. Remember to unplug your refrigerator or freezer when cleaning.
- Do not use scouring powders or abrasive cleaners. A warm water and baking soda solution is a good cleaner.
- Wipe off all spills immediately. Certain foods with an acid content could cause stains.
- Defrost when frost becomes one quarter inch thick on walls of freezer compartment. A large frost build-up results in inefficient operation.

Machine compartment maintenance
- Clean the defrost drain pan at least once a year. A warm water and baking soda solution is a good cleaner and will help eliminate odors.
- Clean the condenser at least once a year for peak operating efficiency. A lint clogged condenser can increase the run time of your appliance.

Food storage tips
- Store foods in the proper compartments for peak flavor. Leafy vegetables, green beans, and citrus fruits stay fresh longer when stored in a moist environment in the vegetable bin.
- Some models have a Cool 'n Fresh Compartment. Use this compartment to store apples, grapes, mushrooms and the like. This is a lower humidity pan which allows air circulation.
- Refrigerate only those meats you plan to use in a day or two. Use the freezer section for longer storage.
- Wrap or cover all food to prevent odor transfer.

- Organize food storage for convenience. Store all like things together and rotate foods using the oldest first. Put frequently used items in front or in door shelves.
- Freeze only top quality foods in freezer packaging.

General maintenance guidelines
- If items stored in either the fresh food or freezer section of the appliance are either too warm or too cold, adjust the temperature according to instructions on the temperature control console.
- For most economical operation, temperatures in the fresh food section should be between 38 and 42 degrees. Temperature can be adjusted as desired. However, make only one adjustment at a time, and then wait 24 hours before readjusting.
- On most single control models, set control at "5" initially. On dual control models, set control at "5" and "C". Adjust as needed.

Icemaker tips
- Turn icemaker control to "OFF" if ice is not needed for an extended period of time, such as vacations, etc.
- Discard first few batches of ice cubes after icemaker has been disconnected for any extended period.
- Use cubes frequently to maintain best quality cubes.
- Do not allow ice bin to remain out of freezer any longer than necessary. Cubes will fuse together.

Preventive maintenance (continued)

Cleaning tips

- Clean the inside of your appliance at least once a year using a solution of one tablespoon baking soda to one quart of warm water.
- Keep an open box of baking soda in the fresh food compartment to help absorb odors. Replace monthly.
- Prevent or remove odors from food particles in the freezer drain of side-by-side models by flushing drain opening at bottom of freezer with two cups of very hot (not boiling) water. For best results use a bulb type meat baster to pump water in under pressure.
- Exterior smudges or discoloration from day-to-day use can be removed with appliance polish wax or mild detergent and water.
- To help remove rust and stains on shelves caused by food spills or moisture, allow shelves to soak in solution of one half cup vinegar to one pint water for thirty minutes. Rinse and dry.

Energy saving tips

- If your appliance has an energy switch, be sure to take advantage of its benefits. Keep the switch in the "Energy Saving" position and change it only if moisture appears on the refrigerator exterior. Resetting switch to "ON" position activates hidden cabinet heaters that prevent condensation.
- Store only those foods that require refrigeration.
- Don't overcrowd your appliance. Refrigerators that are overcrowded can require extra electrical energy to keep everything cold.
- Allow warm or hot foods to cool before placing them in refrigerator or freezer.
- Don't neglect an old model in your basement or garage. It uses electrical energy, and if it isn't really necessary, don't use it.

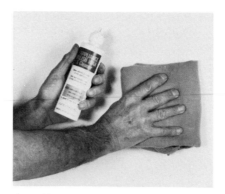

Appliance polishing

- Unusual or lasting odors may indicate food spoilage. Empty appliance and lift out removable parts. Wash thoroughly with baking soda and water solution. Keep excess water away from switches and controls. Dry completely.

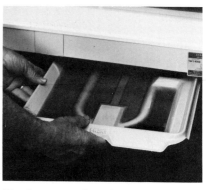

Drain pan cleaning

- Clean the defrost pan beneath your refrigerator at least once a year with a mixture of one tablespoon baking soda and one quart warm water. Note: Some defrost pans are not removable nor are they dishwasher safe.

Energy Saver switch

- Locate your refrigerator or freezer with care. Avoid direct sunlight or installation near the range or laundry equipment.
- Check to make sure all doors are properly cleaned and are sealing properly.

- Try to eliminate unnecessary opening of door. Close the door as soon as possible, especially in hot, humid weather.
- Wipe all moisture from bottles and cartons before placing them in the refrigerator or freezer.

Tools and testing equipment

Tools

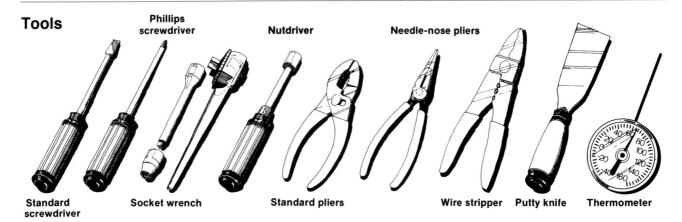

Phillips screwdriver

Nutdriver

Needle-nose pliers

Standard screwdriver

Socket wrench

Standard pliers

Wire stripper

Putty knife

Thermometer

Chances are you already have some of the above tools in your home. For safety and efficiency reasons it is important to use the proper tools when making repairs to your freezer or refrigerator. The tool you will use the most is the screwdriver. Various sizes of standard and Phillips screwdrivers will be necessary to remove the many screws on your appliance.

Some screws and nuts, especially those used on access panels, have hexagonal heads without slots. To remove these, you will need either a nutdriver or socket wrench. The nutdriver is made like a screwdriver but has a small socket on one end. This socket fits over the hexagon head of the screw or nut. It's used just like a screwdriver.

The socket wrench usually has a handle with a rachet that can be set to tighten or loosen a nut, an extension, and various sockets. Sockets usually come in a set containing several sizes , but the 1/4 inch and 5/16 inch are the most commonly used on refrigerators and freezers.

To use a socket wrench, place the socket on the nut and turn the handle counter-clockwise to loosen it. If it makes a clicking

sound and does not turn, flip the rachet lever to the opposite direction and loosen the nut.

The putty knife will be used to remove breaker strips on your refrigerator or freezer. The knife should be approximately 1-1/2 inches wide. A piece of tape over the blade will prevent you from marring the surface of your appliance.

A refrigeration thermostat is an optional, but handy instrument to have. It is essential for temperature testing. The dial thermometer shown above is easy to read, but the standard liquid-filled type is less costly.

Testing equipment

An ohmmeter is required to diagnose the electrical components of your freezer or refrigerator. The ohmmeter is a simple device that measures the amount of resistance in an electrical circuit. Ohmmeters are usually combined with a voltmeter into an instrument called a multimeter, multitester, or volt-ohmmeter (VOM). Volt-ohmmeters can measure the amount of both resistance and voltage in an electrical circuit. A simple, inexpensive ohmmeter will be sufficient for any refrigeration repairs presented in this manual. No operation in this manual requires ohmmeter testing with the appliance plugged in.

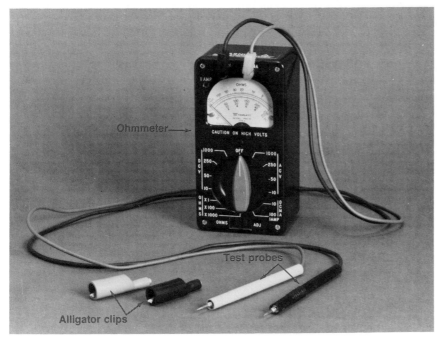

Ohmmeter

Test probes

Alligator clips

Ohmmeter

Tools and testing equipment (continued)

Most problems that occur in an electrical circuit are invisible. For example, it is difficult to see contacts that are not closing inside a switch, or to find a break in the resistance wire inside the heating unit. For the most part, you'll be using the ohmmeter only as a continuity tester to determine whether or not current can pass through the circuit. By passing a small electrical current from a battery contained inside the ohmmeter through the circuit, you can tell if the circuit is complete.

To understand the basic flow of electricity, think of it in terms of a water pumping station. In order for water to flow through the pipes, it must have a complete "closed loop" from the

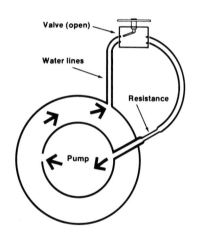

pump, through the valves, then back to the pump again. If the line is broken or opened at any point, water would eventually cease to flow.

The flow of electricity through your freezer or refrigerator is similar to the pumping of water, except electrons rather than water are flowing through the circuitry. The pump is the wall receptacle that provides the force to circulate current. The electrical circuit uses wires rather than

pipes as the conductors of electricity and switches rather than valves to control the flow. Voltage is comparable to the pressure that exists in a water circuit, while electrical current could be compared to the flow rate of water that flows through the pipe.

Some tests with an ohmmeter will be needed for repair procedures presented in this manual. An ohmmeter will have either a switch or pair of jacks (plugs) that allow you to select the function of the meter. Resistance is measured in units called ohms and will be designated by the symbol Ω, or

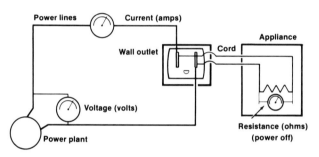

the letter R. Your meter may have more than one range scale. When set at R × 1, the reading should be taken directly from the meter. When set at a higher scale, such as R × 100, the reading on the scale should be multiplied by 100 to obtain the correct resistance. Most measurements for testing components or circuits are made on the lowest scale, usually R × 1.

Plug the test leads in the jacks marked "ohms". The red lead goes in the positive (+) jack and the black on to negative (−). If your meter gives you a choice of functions, select the range first, then "zero" the meter by touching the two test probes together. With the probes tightly in contact with each other, the needle of the meter should

sweep towards "O" (zero) resistance. Now, while holding the probes together, adjust the knob marked "zero adjust" or "ohms adjust" until the needle rests directly over "O".

At this point, you can see exactly how the meter works. If instead of touching the probes together you touch them to each end of a wire, or to a fuse, the needle should sweep toward "O". This indicates that the wire or fuse will conduct electricity. But if the wire or fuse is broken inside, the needle would not move. When this condition exists in a component or circuit, it is said to be "open", and it

cannot conduct electricity. But if the needle moves to indicate that it does conduct electricity, then the component or circuit is said to have "continuity".

All wires in the electrical circuit should indicate "O" resistance when tested in this manner. Switches should indicate "O" resistance when they're turned on, and should be open when turned off. Components that do work such as heating units and fan motors will offer some electrical resistance, but will not be open. The meter reading for these instances should be somewhere between full scale and no reading. The circuit diagram for your specific appliance will indicate the approximate resistance value for each of these components.

Many repair procedures in this manual advise you to test for grounds when checking a component. When doing this, you should select the highest resistance scale on the ohmmeter. You will be directed to place one test probe on a terminal of the component and the other test probe on a metallic portion of the component housing. No current should flow through those paths; if the meter indicates that continuity exists under those conditions, the component is grounded and should be replaced.

The repair procedures in this manual will show you the test points (where to place the test probes) for various tests. You'll find the ohmmeter to be a valuable addition to your home tool collection. For further information on the function and operation of an ohmmeter, see pages 96 and 97.

Using the ohmmeter

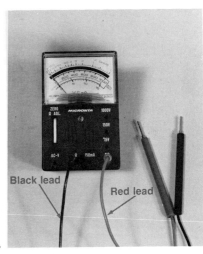

Full-featured ohmmeter like the one shown has numerous switch-selected ranges. Note that ohms scale at top is reversed--zero resistance is at full sweep upscale.

Inexpensive ohmmeters using jacks rather than switches to select function, still provide zero ohms adjustment. Note that red lead plugs into positive (+) jack, black into negative (−).

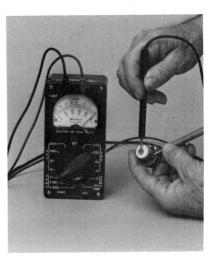

To zero ohmmeter, touch probes tightly together and turn zero adjusting knob until needle is centered over "0" (ZERO) at full sweep of scale. This adjusts readout to the battery condition and to the resistance selected.

Sometimes you can't identify a blown fuse, even when it has a glass shell. Saving a single service call for a simple problem like this can pay for the price of a meter.

CAUTION: Do not attempt to test resistance of any circuit with the power turned on: Checking a live voltage circuit will damage your testing meter.

How to interpret circuit diagrams

The circuit diagram that accompanies your refrigerator or freezer shows how wiring is connected between components and how the internal electrical circuitry of the components is arranged. The secret to using a circuit diagram as a diagnostic tool is to simplify the diagram. When reading a circuit diagram, focus your attention only on that part of the diagram that involves the area you are testing.

Circuit diagrams may be drawn in several different ways. Some component symbols may be different, but all show the path of the current from the lines through the switches and components. This flow of current depicts the continuous loop required to complete an electrical circuit.

Interpreting your refrigerator or freezer diagram is not difficult once you know certain basic facts, symbols, and abbreviations. Relevant symbols are listed at the bottom of this page. Wires are color coded for easy identification. The terminals of most switches and other components are identified by either numbers or letters such as those on the defrost control. Remember, however, when you are reading a circuit diagram to note only the path the electricity flows. The circuit diagram does not indicate location of components as they would actually be found in the refrigerator. Refer to the pictorial wiring diagram for actual location of components and wires. (See Figure 1. as an example)

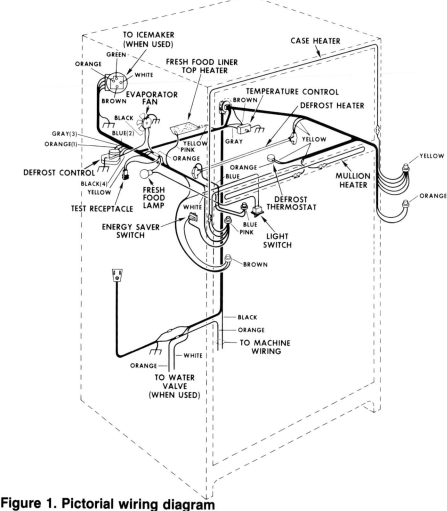

Figure 1. Pictorial wiring diagram

Symbols

The following Legend of Symbols will assist you in reading the circuit diagram of your appliance.

POWER CORD		**WIRES CONNECTED**	
HEATING UNIT		**WIRES CROSSING**	
LIGHT		**OPTIONAL WIRING**	
OVERLOAD		**CIRCULAR MOTION**	
SOLENOID OR MOTOR WINDING		**SELF-CONTAINED UNIT**	
SWITCH OR CONTACT		**OHMS**	
THERMOSTAT		**MALE-FEMALE DISCONNECTS**	

For explanation purposes, let's study closely the circuit diagram for a refrigerator (Figure 1). The power supply is shown entering at the top of the diagram. Notice at the bottom of the plug, there is a symbol indicating the ground or third wire in the power cord. The other two wires in the plug flow in parallel lines on each side of the diagram. The main wire at the left is the hot line which carries current from the plug to the various components of the refrigerator. The line on the right completes the loop by returning the power. This line is called the neutral or common line. By simply tracing the main line around, you can see how current flows through the various components in a closed circuit.

Now trace the flow of current by following the hot line to the temperature control switch. When the switch is closed, the current flows to the defrost control and on to terminal number 4. After the current passes through the Guardette® protector, it goes to both the condenser fan motor windings and also through the relay coil run winding where it creates a magnetic reaction. This reaction closes the switch inside the relay which allows current to flow through to the start winding of the compressor motor. At this point, the refrigeration process begins. Remember, when a switch or contact is closed, current can flow uninterrupted. However, when a switch is open, current ceases to flow.

Look again at the hot line. Follow the hot line through the temperature control to the defrost control. When the

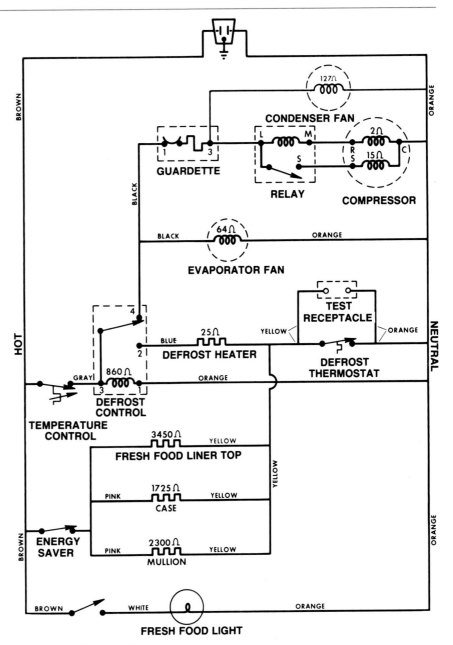

Figure 2. Circuit diagram

defrost control is in defrost cycle, the switch will connect to terminal number 2, allowing current to flow to the defrost heater. By looking at your circuit diagram, you may liken it to a roadmap. You can then follow the power "route" to the door switch, the evaporator fan, or other components. By referring to your circuit diagram as a guide, you can use the ohmmeter to check the contacts that should be closed in each

position. If they don't correspond to values on the circuit diagram, then the component should be replaced.

You can find a copy of your circuit diagram either glued to the back of your refrigerator or freezer, or in an envelope located behind the grille. By learning to read the circuit diagram for your appliance and using your ohmmeter, you can pinpoint problems with operation.

Refrigerator and freezer accessories

In addition to supplying quality original replacement parts for your refrigerator or freezer, GE also provides a variety of useful refrigerator and freezer accessories. Some accessories are replacement items that help keep your appliance looking and working like new, while others let you add new convenience features. The most popular and widely available refrigerator and freezer accessories are featured below.

Appliance paint

High quality paints in spray cans and touch-up applicators are available in five colors to match GE/Hotpoint appliances. Camouflaging most nicks and scratches, GE appliance paint is an easy-to-use and long-lasting way to improve your refrigerator or freezer's appearance.

Appliance wax and cleaner

Protective liquid wax contains silicone sealant to clean, polish and wax in one easy step. The 8-oz. squeeze bottle contains enough liquid wax for several applications to keep your refrigerator or freezer finish in like-new condition.
WR97X216A

Light bulbs

Replacement light bulbs for your appliance are available from GE. Supplied according to specifications for GE/Hotpoint refrigerators, bulbs are specifically designed to withstand cold temperatures.

Coil brush

Refrigerator coil brush is especially shaped to clean in hard to reach spaces to help reduce energy consumption, while improving refrigerator efficiency. Long handled brush is tapered with dense washable bristles to clean where vacuum can't.
WX14X51A

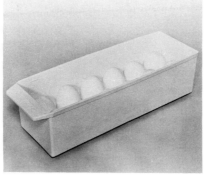

Egg rack

Handy "carton" size rack will hold one dozen eggs at fingertip convenience on door or interior shelves. Special molded indentions help keep eggs from cracking or breaking. Dishwasher safe on top rack.

Butter dish

Easy-store butter dish holds a stick of butter for service from refrigerator to table. It's convenient size fits neatly in butter keeper or on shelves. Crack resistant at cold temperatures, butter dish is dishwasher safe on top rack.

Ice trays

One twist and ice cubes pop loose. Set of two stackable trays utilize freezer space and are coated with a special film to provide easy release of cubes. Each crack-resistant tray makes 14 uniform cubes.

WR30X196A

Ice tray and bin

Easy release trays provide ice with a minimum of effort, while storage bin allows for convenience of larger quantities of ice. Trays are designed to stack on top of bin to allow for optimum use of freezer space. All pieces are durable and crack-resistant at cold temperatures.

WR30X173A

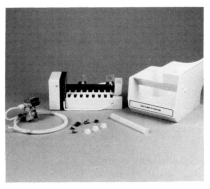

Icemaker kit

Enjoy the convenience of automatic ice making. Ice cubes are replaced as you use them to help keep you readily supplied with a binful of cubes. For replacement or new service, the GE icemaker's quiet operation and plentiful ice supply will add extra benefits to your present refrigerator.

Water supply kit

Kit contains all the necessary parts to connect your automatic icemaker to household cold water lines. Complete with twenty feet of flexible copper tubing, saddle valve with shut-off, and fittings, water supply kit helps simplify water line installation.

WX8X3A

Water filter

Helps produce fresher tasting water to keep ice cubes clear and uniform in size by removing impurities that interfere with freezing process. Water filter helps remove oil and chemical taste while protecting icemaker and water valves from scale deposits.

WR97X214A

Water filter replacement cartriges

Cartriges are easily replaced without water line disconnection. Their activated charcoal filter helps remove sediment, unpleasant taste, and scale from water to improve water quality and keep your icemaker functioning properly.

WR97X215A

Glossary of terms

Access cover
Metal or fiberboard cover at rear of appliance used to enclose wiring and/or electromechanical components.

Ambient
Surrounding air or room temperature.

Baffle
Device used in a refrigerator to deflect air flow.

Bell connector
Solderless connector for splicing wiring. Insulating cover crimps onto twisted ends of wires to assure solid connection.

Bellows
Mechanism inside the temperature control that expands and contracts as temperature is increased or decreased.

Bimetal limit switch
Temperature sensitive device used to provide protection against overheating.

Bracket
A rigid structure designed to affix or support a component.

Breaker
Plastic strip used to reduce heat transfer from outside cabinet to inner liner of refrigerator or freezer.

Cabinet
Outside body of refrigerator or freezer.

Capillary tube
Very small diameter tube that allows liquid to be metered under pressure.

Circuit
Path of electrical current from power supply through wiring to point of use and back to source.

Circuit breaker
Device to protect circuit from current overload. "Tripped" circuit breaker interrupts circuit when current exceeds specified amount. See also FUSE.

Circuit diagram
Drawing using standard symbols to represent path of current flow from power supply through switches and components and back to source. Shows how wiring is connected between components and how internal wiring of components is arranged.

Closed (circuit)
Complete circuit which can conduct electricity.

Component

An individual electrical or mechanical part of a refrigerator system.

Compressor

Device similar to a pump used for increasing the pressure of refrigerant vapor in the condenser.

Condenser

Device that condenses (converts) a refrigerant vapor to a liquid by giving up heat.

Connector

Any device on the end of a wire to facilitate either connection or disconnection.

Contact

Switch component which opens and closes to complete or break an electrical circuit.

Continuity

Ability of completed circuit to conduct electricity.

Defective

In this manual, used to mean a component which does not function properly and which must be replaced.

Distribution panel

Fuse or circuit breaker box that distributes incoming power from outside line into a number of household circuits.

Dual function

Having two functions.

Energize

To supply electrical current for operation of a component.

Evaporator

A refrigerator or freezer component in which evaporation of refrigerant takes place at a low pressure and subsequently provides a low temperature.

Flange

Piece of protruding metal, plastic, etc. used for mounting purposes or support.

Fuse

Device to protect circuit from current overload. "Blown" fuse automatically interrupts circuit when current exceeds specified amount. See also CIRCUIT BREAKER.

Gasket

Flexible material designed to prevent cold air leakage between components or parts of refrigerator body.

Glossary of terms (continued)

Grommet
A rubber or plastic washer used to protect wires passing through a hole.

Ground
Connection to earth of another conducting body which transmits current to earth. Metal components in a circuit must be grounded to prevent their accidentally becoming electrically charged, causing injury.

Hermetically sealed
An air-tight seal of the compressor and other components of the sealed refrigeration system.

Inoperative
In this manual, used to mean a component which does not function, but which can be checked and possibly repaired.

Lead
Portion of electrical wiring attached to component.

Liner
Inner case of a refrigerator or freezer.

Multiconnector
Connector used to house several male-female connections.

Nutdriver
Tool used to remove and reinstall hexagonal-head screws or nuts. Resembles a screwdriver with a small socket at the end instead of a blade.

Ohm
Measurement unit for electrical resistance.

Ohmmeter
Battery operated test instrument for determining continuity of a circuit and measuring its resistance.

Open (circuit)
Incomplete circuit which cannot conduct electricity.

Refrigerant
A substance that by undergoing a change in state (liquid to gas) absorbs heat and produces a cooling effect.

Refrigeration
The cooling of a space or substance below environmental temperature.

Resistance
Restriction of current in an electrical circuit.

Retainer strip
Metal or plastic strip used to hold another object in place.

Sealant
An adhesive agent used to prevent seepage of moisture or air.

Shield
A protective metal plate or similar hard outer covering.

Short circuit
Accidentally created circuit between hot wire and any ground, allowing excessive current flow with little or no resistance.

Solenoid
Cylindrical coil of insulated wire that establishes a magnetic field in the presence of current.

Switch
Device to turn current on and off in an electrical circuit.

Terminal
Connection point between wiring and electrical components. Commonly used terminals in refrigerators and freezers are push-on terminals, which are held in place by their snug fit.

Test probes
Metal components of ohmmeter which are attached to each end of a circuit during testing for continuity or resistance. See OHMMETER.

Thermostat
Heat-sensing component that controls temperature levels by turning cooling source on and off.

Upscale
Reading from ohmmeter that indicates continuity in a circuit.

Volt
Measurement unit for electrical pressure.

Watt
Measurement unit for electrical power.

Winding
One or more turns of wire forming a continuous coil for a relay or other rotating machine. A conductive path is formed by the wire.

Index

Index (continued)